Cannabis

Series Editor: Cara Acred

Volume 256

Independen

First published by Independence Educational Publishers

The Studio, High Green

Great Shelford

Cambridge CB22 5EG

England

© Independence 2014

British Library Cataloguing in Publication Data

Cannabis. -- (Issues ; 256)
1. Cannabis. 2. Marijuana. 3. Marijuana abuse.
4. Marijuana--Law and legislation.
I. Series II. Acred, Cara editor of compilation.
362.2'95-dc23

ISBN-13: 9781861686671

Printed in Great Britain
MWL Print Group Ltd

Contents

Introduction

Cannabis is Volume 256 in the **ISSUES** series. The aim of the series is to offer current, diverse information about important issues in our world, from a UK perspective.

ABOUT CANNABIS

Approximately half of all 16- to 29-year-olds have tried cannabis at least once, but it's not just young people dabbling with the drug; 20 million adults also admit to using cannabis in the last year. With some campaigners arguing that cannabis should be legalised for medical and recreational purposes, and others maintaining that it should remain firmly illegal, what are the facts? This book explores the facts about cannabis use, looking at the potential side effects and medical benefits, as well as the varying opinions about its legal status.

OUR SOURCES

Titles in the **ISSUES** series are designed to function as educational resource books, providing a balanced overview of a specific subject.

The information in our books is comprised of facts, articles and opinions from many different sources, including:

⇨ Newspaper reports and opinion pieces

⇨ Website factsheets

⇨ Magazine and journal articles

⇨ Statistics and surveys

⇨ Government reports

⇨ Literature from special interest groups.

A NOTE ON CRITICAL EVALUATION

Because the information reprinted here is from a number of different sources, readers should bear in mind the origin of the text and whether the source is likely to have a particular bias when presenting information (or when conducting their research). It is hoped that, as you read about the many aspects of the issues explored in this book, you will critically evaluate the information presented.

It is important that you decide whether you are being presented with facts or opinions. Does the writer give a biased or unbiased report? If an opinion is being expressed, do you agree with the writer? Is there potential bias to the 'facts' or statistics behind an article?

ASSIGNMENTS

In the back of this book, you will find a selection of assignments designed to help you engage with the articles you have been reading and to explore your own opinions. Some tasks will take longer than others and there is a mixture of design, writing and research-based activities that you can complete alone or in a group.

FURTHER RESEARCH

At the end of each article we have listed its source and a website that you can visit if you would like to conduct your own research. Please remember to critically evaluate any sources that you consult and consider whether the information you are viewing is accurate and unbiased.

Useful weblinks

www.cannabisdependency.co.uk

www.clear-uk.org

www.medic8.com

www.ms-uk.org

www.ncpic.org.au

www.nhs.uk

www.rcpsych.ac.uk

www.talkingdrugs.org

www.talktofrank.com

What is cannabis?

Two million people in the UK smoke cannabis. Half of all 16- to 29-year-olds have tried it at least once. In spite of government warnings about health risks, many people see it as a harmless substance that helps you to relax and 'chill' – a drug that, unlike alcohol and cigarettes, might even be good for your physical and mental health. On the other hand, recent research has suggested that it can be a major cause of psychotic illnesses in those who are genetically vulnerable.

This article looks at the research on the effects of cannabis use and mental health and is for anyone who is concerned about the issue. We hope that this will help people to make informed choices about using – or not using – cannabis.

What is cannabis?

Cannabis sativa and *Cannabis indica* are members of the nettle family that have grown wild throughout the

world for centuries. Both plants have been used for a variety of purposes including hemp to make rope and textiles, as a medical herb and as the popular recreational drug.

The plant is used as:

⇨ The resin – a brown/black lump, known as bhang, ganja, hashish, resin, etc.;

⇨ Herbal cannabis – made up of the dried flowering tops and variable amounts of dried leaves – known as grass, marijuana, spliff, weed, etc.

Skunk refers to a range of stronger types of cannabis, grown for their higher concentration of active substances. The name refers to the pungent smell they give off while growing. They can be grown either under grow-lights or in a greenhouse, often using hydroponic (growing in nutrient-rich liquids rather than soil) techniques. There are hundreds of other varieties of cannabis with exotic names such as AK-47 or Destroyer.

Street cannabis can come in a wide variety of strengths, so it is often not possible to judge exactly what is being used in any one particular session.

How is it used?

Most commonly, the resin or the dried leaves are mixed with tobacco and smoked as a 'spliff' or 'joint'. The smoke is inhaled strongly and held in the lungs for a number of seconds. It can also be smoked in a pipe, a water pipe or collected in a container before inhaling it – a 'bucket'. It can be brewed as tea or cooked in cakes.

More than half of its psychologically active chemical ingredients are absorbed into the blood when smoked. These compounds tend to build up in fatty tissues throughout the body, so it takes a long time to be excreted in the urine. This is why cannabis can be detected in urine up to 56 days after it has last been used.

What is its legal status in the UK?

Cannabis was re-classified in January 2009 and is now a Class B drug under the Misuse of Drugs Act, 1971.

The maximum penalties are:

⇨ For possession: five years prison sentence or an unlimited fine, or both.

⇨ For dealing/supplying: 14-year prison sentence or an unlimited fine, or both.

Young people in possession of cannabis

A young person found to be in possession of cannabis will be:

⇨ Arrested.

⇨ Taken to a police station.

⇨ Given a reprimand, final warning or charge, depending on the offence.

⇨ After one reprimand, a further offence will lead to a final warning or charge.

After a final warning:

⇨ The young person must be referred to a Youth Offending Team to arrange a rehabilitation programme.

⇨ A further offence will lead to a criminal charge.

Adults in possession of cannabis

This will usually result in a warning and confiscation of the drug. Some cases may lead to arrest and either caution or prosecution, including:

⇨ repeat offending

⇨ smoking in a public place

⇨ threatening public order.

How does it work and what is the chemical make-up of cannabis?

There are about 400 chemical compounds in an average cannabis plant. The four main compounds are called delta-9-tetrahydrocannabinol (delta-9-THC), cannabidiol, delta-8-tetrahydrocannabinol and cannabinol. Apart from cannabidiol (CBD), these compounds are psychoactive, the strongest one being delta-9-tetrahydrocannabinol. The stronger varieties of the plant contain little cannabidiol (CBD), whilst the delta-9-THC content is a lot higher.

When cannabis is smoked, its compounds rapidly enter the bloodstream and are transported directly to the brain and other parts of the body. The feeling of being 'stoned' or 'high' is caused mainly by the delta-9-THC binding to cannabinoid receptors in the brain. A receptor is a site on a brain cell where certain substances can stick or 'bind' for a while. If this happens, it has an effect on the cell and the nerve impulses it produces. Curiously, there are also cannabis-like substances produced naturally by the brain itself – these are called endocannabinoids.

Most of these receptors are found in the parts of the brain that influence pleasure, memory, thought, concentration, sensory and time perception. Cannabis compounds can also affect the eyes, the ears, the skin and the stomach.

November 2012

⇨ The above information is reprinted with kind permission from the Royal College of Psychiatrists. Please visit www.rcpsych.ac.uk for further information.

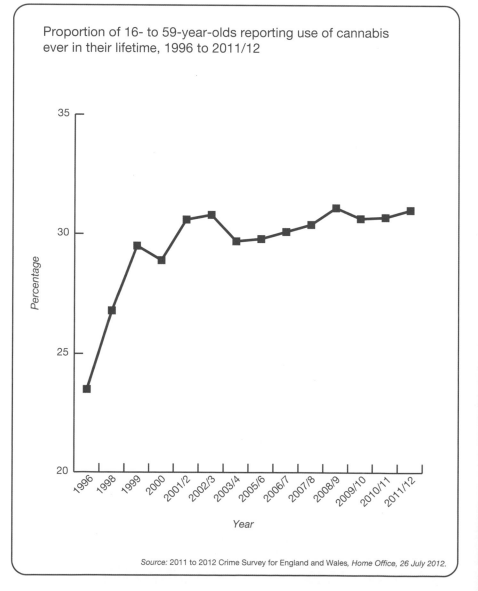

Proportion of 16- to 59-year-olds reporting use of cannabis ever in their lifetime, 1996 to 2011/12

Source: 2011 to 2012 Crime Survey for England and Wales, *Home Office*, 26 July 2012.

Synthetic cannabinoids

Related terms: X, Tai High Hawaiian Haze, Spice, Mary Joy, Exodus Damnation, Ecsess, Devil's Weed, Clockwork Orange, Bombay Blue Extreme, Blue Cheese, Black Mamba, Annihilation, Amsterdam Gold.

The drug

Overview

Synthetic cannabinoids are chemicals that are made to act like the active part of cannabis, a substance called tetrahydrocannabinol (THC). As synthetic cannabinoids act like cannabis, the effects – good and bad – are likely to be very similar to cannabis. Some users will feel happy and relaxed, may get the giggles, feel hunger pangs and become very talkative. Others may feel ill or paranoid.

Synthetic cannabinoids are usually sold in 'herbal' smoking mixtures. Sometimes these smoking mixtures have been found not to contain any synthetic cannabinoids at all!

There are lots of different types of synthetic cannabinoids and a large number have become Class B drugs, which are illegal to have, give away or sell. You can never be sure what is in a smoking mixture so it's often hard to tell whether it is illegal or not.

Appearance

In their pure form, synthetic cannabinoids are either solids or oils. They are then added to dried herbs, vegetable matter or plant cuttings to make a smoking mixture (so that it looks more like real herbal cannabis).

The smoking mixtures are packaged very professionally in small, often colourful sachets with labels describing the contents as incense or herbal smoking mixture and almost always stating: 'Not for human consumption'.

There are many different names given to herbal smoking mixtures, some of the most common are listed at the top of the page.

Although there are many different names or brands it is not uncommon for different brands to contain the same synthetic cannabinoids. Some may even contain illegal synthetic cannabinoids.

Use

How do people take synthetic cannabinoids?

Synthetic cannabinoids are used in a similar way to cannabis:

⇨ They can be mixed with tobacco, rolled up into something known as a 'spliff' or a 'joint', and then smoked.

⇨ They can be smoked without tobacco using a type of pipe called a bong.

The effects

What are the effects of synthetic cannabinoids?

Synthetic cannabinoids act like THC, the active substance in cannabis. They may be stronger than typical cannabis and because these substances are so new, they may have completely unknown effects. Typical cannabis effects include:

⇨ Some can make you feel happy and relaxed. Some people may get the giggles, feel hunger pangs and become very talkative. Others get more drowsy.

⇨ Mood and perception can change and concentration and coordination may become difficult.

⇨ Some will have quite bad reactions. Paranoia, panic attacks and forgetfulness are all associated with using cannabis.

The risks

What are the risks?

What are the risks of synthetic cannabinoids?

Because synthetic cannabinoids act like THC, the main active ingredient in cannabis, it is very likely that they will produce harmful effects similar to those associated with cannabis. But many synthetic cannabinoids are new and may have other completely unknown effects too. There may also be risks from smoking the plant material itself – as occurs with tobacco and cannabis smoking.

⇨ Regular use of products containing synthetic cannabinoids may increase the risk of later developing psychotic illnesses including schizophrenia.

⇨ Experts are concerned that synthetic cannabinoids have the potential to be more harmful than cannabis because of the high strength of these compounds compared to cannabis and because of the range of different chemicals being produced.

⇨ The effects of some of the synthetic cannabinoids may be longer lasting than cannabis and because of the lack of information about what is in the smoking mixtures it may be difficult to predict the strength of different products.

⇨ Anecdotal reports about the synthetic cannabinoid AM2201 suggest that it can cause an increased heart rate, panic attacks and convulsions. It is likely that other synthetic cannabinoids will have similar adverse effects.

⇨ From anecdotal and official reports, the most common

risks from using synthetic cannabinoids are an increase in heart rate, feeling on edge or restless, feeling tired or drowsy, feeling sick, being sick and hallucinations (seeing and/or hearing things that aren't there).

Impurities

What are synthetic cannabinoids cut with?

Any dried herbs, vegetable matter or plant cuttings can be used to make smoking mixtures. A number of different plants are often listed on the packaging of smoking mixtures, but it appears that many are not present and that the packaging cannot be trusted. The chemical composition of synthetic cannabinoids and the ingredients of smoking mixtures are changing all the time, so you can never be sure what you're getting, how powerful it is and how it could affect you.

There have been very few studies carried out on the level of synthetic cannabinoids present in smoking mixtures. Because of the difficulties in making a smoking mixture it is likely that there will be differences in the concentration of synthetic cannabinoids between different batches. Some don't contain any synthetic cannabinoids at all.

Getting hooked

Can you get addicted to synthetic cannabinoids?

There is little information about whether synthetic cannabinoids are addictive. However, because they are similar to cannabis, which is addictive, it is likely that dependence on synthetic cannabinoids is a real risk for users.

Dependence will be influenced by a number of factors, including how long you've been using it, how much you use and whether you are just more prone to become dependent.

If you have used synthetic cannabinoids regularly you may find it difficult to stop using and you may experience psychological and physical withdrawals when you do stop. The withdrawals can include cravings for synthetic cannabinoids, irritability, mood changes, loss of appetite, weight loss, difficulty sleeping and even sweating, shaking and diarrhoea.

The law

Synthetic cannabinoids and the law

⇨ A large number of synthetic cannabinoids and any mixtures that contain these synthetic cannabinoids, including Black Mamba and Annihilation, are Class B drugs and are illegal to have, give away or sell. Some products have been found to contain synthetic cannabinoids that are currently legal to possess, but as you can't be sure what's in any smoking mixture, when you purchase one you always run the risk that you may be in possession of a Class B drug.

⇨ Possession of products containing controlled synthetic cannabinoids can get you up to five years in jail and/or an unlimited fine.

⇨ Supplying someone else, including your friends, can get you 14 years in jail and/or an unlimited fine.

What if you're caught?

⇨ If the police catch you with controlled synthetic cannabinoids, they'll always take some action. This could include a formal caution, arrest and prosecution.

⇨ A conviction for a drug-related offence could have a serious impact. It can stop you visiting certain countries – for example the United States – and limit the types of jobs you can apply for.

Did you know?

⇨ Like drinking and driving, driving when under the influence of drugs is illegal – in fact you can still be unfit to drive the day after using some drugs, especially if you've been up all night. You can get a heavy fine, be disqualified from driving or even go to prison.

⇨ Allowing other people to use drugs in your house or any other premises is illegal. If the police catch someone they can prosecute the landlord, club owner or person holding the party.

⇨ The above information is reprinted with kind permission from FRANK. For friendly, confidential information and advice about drugs you can Talk to FRANK on 0300 123 6600 or visit www.talktofrank.com.

© FRANK 2011

Young people and marijuana

Marijuana is a popular drug of choice with young people, which is mainly due to its easy availability and low cost. It can be grown at home or in outdoor locations which have been chosen for that purpose and is seen as less harmful than other recreational drugs.

Many young people consider using marijuana to be no worse than having a few drinks or a cigarette. In fact they often claim that it causes less harm than these two and should be legalised.

A higher percentage of boys than girls use marijuana although this is minimal. Older teens are more likely to use it than younger teens.

Marijuana as a coping mechanism

Many young people use marijuana as a means of coping with certain pressures in their lives such as exams, relationships, etc. They also use it as way of relieving boredom, frustration, anxiety or anger and as a means of escapism.

It can be seen as a way of dealing with the ups and downs of growing up but there are other less harmful ways of doing so. Any problems the young person has, must be faced and dealt with rather than ignored or run away from.

If a young person has been physically or sexually abused then there is an increased risk of them using marijuana and at an earlier age compared to other young people.

Why do so many young people use marijuana?

There are several reasons for this, including:

⇨ peer pressure

⇨ rebellion

⇨ curiosity

⇨ genetic predisposition

⇨ environment.

Peer pressure

Peer pressure is one of the main reasons for trying marijuana. Many young people experiment with drugs in order to fit in with their peer group or because it is seen as a cool and daring thing to do.

Being part of a group often means wearing the right clothes, having similar hairstyles and liking the same music. If the group smokes marijuana or uses other drugs then part of being that group means doing the same. There can be pressure to do so and many young people will try drugs rather than be excluded from the group.

This is a stage where they have a strong desire to belong and not stand out from the rest of the crowd.

Rebellion

Marijuana is often used as a form of rebellion against authority. Knowing that your parents, teachers or other authority figures disapprove of this makes it even more attractive.

This is not new: young people have been rebelling against authority for decades and using drugs such as marijuana is one way of doing so.

Adolescence is a time when young people test boundaries; they are exploring their identities and trying to assert themselves in a variety of ways. It is a time of raging hormones and other changes which can be confusing and difficult to deal with.

The young person is on the cusp of adulthood and is trying to adapt to

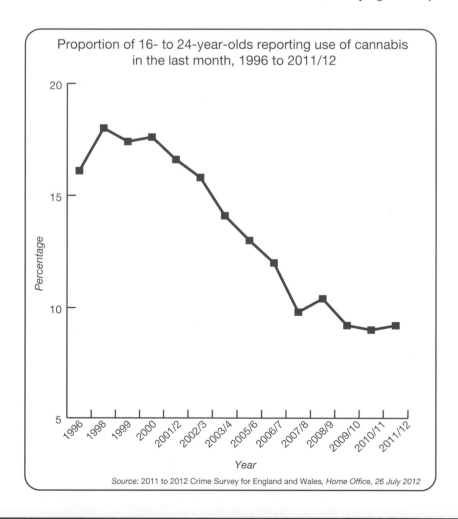

Proportion of 16- to 24-year-olds reporting use of cannabis in the last month, 1996 to 2011/12

Source: 2011 to 2012 Crime Survey for England and Wales, Home Office, 26 July 2012

the challenges that brings. Using marijuana is one way of coping with that.

Curiosity

Young people try drugs such as marijuana to see what they are like. They are at a stage where they want to be adults and to try adult things, which include cigarettes, alcohol and drugs.

Genetic predisposition

Some people have what is called an 'addictive personality' which means that they are vulnerable to the effects of substances such as alcohol and drugs.

If a member of their family has used marijuana then there is a strong chance that they will do the same.

There are people who are more likely to become addicted to marijuana than others due to the way their brains are wired. They may be more likely to develop anxiety or depression or use drugs such as marijuana as a way of dealing with stress.

Environmental

If a young person grows up in a home where other people use drugs such as marijuana or their household is considered dysfunctional or chaotic then marijuana may be used as a form of escapism.

If they are brought up to see drug taking as normal and acceptable then there is a good chance that they will do the same.

Risk of addiction

It has been found that if a young person smokes tobacco then there is a strong likelihood that they will use marijuana as well. The danger is that this could lead to the use of stronger substances such as heroin, crack or cocaine.

Young people do not have sufficient maturity to understand the dangers of marijuana use and the possibility that it could lead to the use of stronger drugs such as heroin.

Young people often assume that they are immortal and that nothing will happen to them. They do not always consider the consequences of their actions and think that nothing will go wrong.

Addiction may not cross their minds or, if it does, is not taken seriously.

Not every person who uses marijuana will become addicted but some people do, so it is important to be aware of this risk.

If you are the parent of a young person who you suspect has been using marijuana then what can you do?

Options include talking to specialist drugs information and advice services such as FRANK (www.talktofrank. com).

⇨ The above information is reprinted with kind permission from Medic8. Please visit www.medic8.com for further information.

© Medic8 ®

Short history of marijuana

Marijuana has a long history which can be traced back as far as ancient Egypt. There is evidence to show that marijuana plant seeds were burnt and inhaled possibly as part of an ancient ritual.

Ancient world

The hallucinogenic properties of marijuana were very popular in parts of the ancient world, including India and Nepal. It was used as part of their religious ceremonies to induce a trance-like state.

China

In the 1st century AD the Chinese used marijuana for its medicinal qualities. Marijuana formed part of many herbal remedies at that time and was a commonly used substance.

India and the Middle East

The use of marijuana as a medicine spread to other parts of the world such as India and the Middle East. But it also had a range of other uses, including recreation, religious ceremonies and manufacture.

Hemp fibre was harvested from marijuana plants to make clothes, ropes, sacks, mats and fishing nets.

Western Europe

In the 19th century soldiers from Napoleon's army brought marijuana with them from their time spent fighting in North Africa. This was the first introduction of marijuana as a recreational drug to Western Europe.

It was also used for medicinal purposes at that time. One example of this was the use of marijuana as a painkiller during childbirth or to ease the pain of menstruation.

Marijuana formed an important part of many herbal remedies in the late 19th and early 20th centuries.

20th century UK

This situation changed in the early part of the 20th century. In the 1920s, recreational use of marijuana was banned in the UK: this occurred following an international conference in which the negative effects of marijuana were highlighted.

It was also banned in several other countries such as South Africa, Canada and New Zealand.

The dangers of marijuana were a common theme throughout the 1930s and 1940s although this was prevalent in the US rather than the UK.

Marijuana was not widely used in the UK during that period although it was a part of the 1950s beatnik scene and the Rastafarian movement.

It experienced a sudden surge in popularity during the 1960s – the emergence of 'hippy culture' – and was mainly used by students in the UK and other countries.

The Misuse of Drugs Act came into force in 1971 which classified marijuana as a Class C drugs, although it has since been upgraded to a Class B drug.

The 1970s saw another surge in use of marijuana due to the influence of reggae music plus another surge in use during the 1990s.

21st century UK

Marijuana remains a popular drug of choice for many people, who use it for its relaxing, mood-enhancing effects.

There is evidence to show that the popularity of marijuana is decreasing amongst young people in the UK. This refers to people who would normally smoke marijuana via a joint or bong (pipe) but are less likely to do so in the light of the recent smoking ban. Smoking in general is seen as less socially acceptable than it was before, which may also account for this decreased usage.

Attitudes towards smoking have hardened over the last few years which mean that as it less acceptable to smoke in public it is even harder to find somewhere to smoke a joint.

Source: www.cannazine.co.uk: initial source – European Monitoring Centre for Drugs and Drug Addiction

⇨ The above information is reprinted with kind permission from Medic8. Please visit www.medic8.com for further information.

© Medic8 ®

Marijuana facts and fiction

Any subject attracts a good number of 'old wives' tales' and myths and marijuana is no different

There are many misconceptions about marijuana which range from the unusual to the potentially dangerous. This article aims to dispel those myths and shows you the reality behind these.

Myth 1: Marijuana is a harmless drug

Fact 1

Small doses or short-term use is unlikely to cause harm but heavy doses or long-term use can lead to addiction. It can also cause physical and psychological damage and worsen existing mental health conditions such as schizophrenia.

It is not as dangerous as heroin or cocaine but, nevertheless, it does have the potential to cause long-term problems.

Myth 2: Marijuana has never killed anyone

Fact 2

Whilst that is correct there have been cases where someone has died in an accident due to being under the influence of marijuana.

Myth 3: Marijuana is not as dangerous as tobacco

Fact 3

Wrong. Marijuana smoke contains chemicals, toxins, tar and carcinogens which are harmful and increase the risk of cancer. In fact, the level of carcinogens is often higher in marijuana smoke than tobacco smoke, which cannot be ignored.

Marijuana smokers tend to inhale this smoke deeply and for longer which increase the amount of time their lungs are exposed to these substances.

Myth 4: Marijuana is not an addictive drug

Fact 4

Not true. Whilst marijuana does not cause physical dependency, it can result in psychological dependency, especially in people who are considered vulnerable.

Some people have a genetic predisposition towards addiction or what we think of as an 'addictive personality', which means that they are more likely to become addicted.

This also applies to people who suffer from anxiety, depression or some other form of mental illness.

Not every person who uses marijuana will become addicted but there is evidence to show that regular users, long-term users or those who use heavy doses are more likely to do so.

Myth 5: Marijuana kills off brain cells

Fact 5

It does not kill brain cells but it can cause changes in brain structure and function, especially if used for a long period of time. Heavy users of marijuana find that their short-term memory is poor; they have a lack of energy and motivation and find it difficult to learn new things or multitask.

Myth 6: Marijuana causes high blood pressure

Fact 6

There is an element of truth in this as marijuana does cause a small rise in blood pressure almost immediately after ingestion. This occurs if the person is sat down and falls when they stand up which may cause them to faint.

Heavy doses of marijuana cause a drop in blood pressure. This is likely to be a problem for people suffering from high blood pressure or heart disease.

Myth 7: Marijuana is not as popular as it used to be

Fact 7

Marijuana is still a popular drug of choice for many people. Plus there are newer, stronger forms available such as skunk and sinsemilla which cause intense hallucinations.

Many young people use marijuana as it is seen as cheap, easy to obtain and a 'natural drug' which means less risk of additives or adulterants.

It is used to relax or 'chill out' and is seen as less risky than others types of drugs.

Myth 8: Marijuana leads to stronger drugs such as heroin or cocaine

Fact 8

Marijuana is not a 'gateway drug' in that it automatically opens the way to harder substances such as cocaine and heroin.

There are people who have used marijuana but have never tried other drugs; conversely there are some who have tried harder drugs such as heroin and cocaine who have also used marijuana.

There will be a few people who will use marijuana and then go onto stronger drugs such as heroin but they are likely to be the exception rather than the norm.

⇨ The above information is reprinted with kind permission from Medic8. Please visit www. medic8.com for further information.

© Medic8 ®

Looking after a friend on cannabis

Using cannabis can have unpredictable effects.

Some of the unwanted physical and psychological effects that may be experienced by a person when they are 'high' on cannabis may include:

⇨ nausea and vomiting

⇨ anxiety, panic and paranoia.

If you are with someone who is affected by cannabis in this way, you can help.

What can you do if someone is physically sick?

'Greening out' is a term that refers to the situation where people feel sick after smoking cannabis. People can go pale and sweaty, feel dizzy, nauseous and may even start vomiting. They usually feel they have to lie down straight away.

You can assist them by:

⇨ taking them to a quiet place with fresh air

⇨ sitting them in a comfortable position

⇨ giving them a glass of water or something sweet (such as juice or a piece of fruit).

If the person feels so sick that they start to vomit:

⇨ stay with them

⇨ lie them down on their side, not on their back, so they don't choke on their vomit

⇨ keep them in a quiet, safe spot where you can monitor them.

If someone is physically sick it is important that you never leave them on their own, not even for the shortest time. Suffocating on vomit is a very real threat and can lead to an otherwise unnecessary death.

What can you do if someone is experiencing panic attacks, anxiety or paranoia?

Unwanted psychological effects can range from depression to anxiety, which can go on to produce panic attacks and paranoia. Although this can be frightening for the person, most of the time these effects can be managed through reassurance.

If someone you know experiences these problems after they have used cannabis, here are some things you can do to assist them:

⇨ try to calm the person down

⇨ reassure them that these feelings will pass in time

⇨ take them to a safe and quiet place and stay with them

⇨ let them know that you are here to help them. If there is something you can do for them, do it. If they do not calm down, try to distract them with other topics of discussion.

If nothing you do is helping

If there is nothing you can do, and the person continues to feel bad or their condition gets worse, then it is important to get more help. Call 999 or take them to get medical help so that they can be treated quickly and safely.

How can you help prevent this from happening again?

After the effects of cannabis wear off, talk to your friend about what happened, how it affected you and those around you and how this can be prevented in the future.

As a friend, you can do the following things that may help prevent this happening again:

⇨ if your friend has a mental illness such as depression, anxiety or schizophrenia, encourage them not to use cannabis or any other drug, unless prescribed by a doctor

⇨ encourage your friend to seek help from their GP or counsellor about their cannabis use if this happens regularly

⇨ remind them what happened the last time they used cannabis

⇨ suggest they avoid bingeing or polydrug use (using more than one drug at the same time), or anything that will intensify the effects of cannabis

⇨ become involved in other activities with them that do not involve drug use.

For more information please see the NCPIC fast facts booklet *Concerned about someone's cannabis use? Fast facts on how to help*.

Factsheet published 1 June, 2008. Updated 1 October, 2011.

⇨ The above information is reprinted with kind permission from National Cannabis Prevention and Information Centre (NCPIC). Please visit www.ncpic.org.au for further information.

Taxing the UK cannabis market

A recent IDMU report commissioned by CLEAR (Cannabis Law Reform) has demonstrated that the net benefit to the taxpayer of a taxed and regulated cannabis market could range from £3.4 billion to £9.5 billion per annum, with a best estimate of £6.7 billion per year at recent market levels.

The cannabis market

There are between 1.7 million and 3.6 million active cannabis users in the UK consuming between 620 and 1,400 metric tonnes of cannabis each year with an estimated market value of between £2.9 and £8.6 billion per annum. The best estimates are an average 2.7 million active users consuming 1,037 metric tonnes with an estimated street value of £5.9 billion per annum.

The majority of the UK market is accounted for by cannabis domestically produced in the UK, with an estimate of between 167,000 and 410,000 UK growers producing between 390 and 950 metric tonnes of cannabis per annum. The bulk of production is accounted for by large-scale commercial cultivations operating on a continuous basis, although significant quantities of skunk-type cannabis are imported into the UK from Western Europe.

Proposed control regime

A viable alternative control regime to the current prohibition policy could involve regulation and taxation of the cannabis market, involving;

⇨ Excise duty based on the potency of the cannabis purchased – encouraging via pricing the consumption of lower-THC varieties of cannabis.

⇨ Domestic production licences allowing production for personal use within a specified surface area and/or limited wattage of horticultural lighting.

⇨ Licensed commercial production or importation and distribution including a network of bonded warehouses and licensed retailers, similar to but tighter than the existing control regimes for alcohol and tobacco.

Potential tax and duty revenues

Based on estimated excise duty revenues at £1 per gram per 5% THC, VAT on recent total cannabis market values at 20%, licences based on estimated numbers of growers taking one square metre to two square metre licences £200 per square metre per

annum and additional income tax revenues based on £200 per offender per annum (if records expunged), the revenue raised by licensing and taxing cannabis would range from £3.2 billion to £9.2 billion per annum, with an average of £6.4 billion.

Cost savings and new costs

Estimated cost savings to the Criminal Justice System would fall between £293 million and £646 million per annum with an average of £512 million. New costs of a compliance regime and collections are estimated at between £157 million and £317 million per annum, with an average of £214 million.

Overall cost benefit

Overall, the net benefit to the taxpayer of a taxed and regulated cannabis market could range from £3.4 billion to £9.5 billion per annum, with a best estimate of £6.7 billion per year at recent market levels.

3 September 2012

⇨ The above information is reprinted with kind permission from Independent Drug Monitoring Unit. Please visit www.idmu.co.uk for further information.

Chapter 2

Cannabis and health

What are the effects of cannabis?

What are its effects?

Pleasant

A 'high' – a sense of relaxation, happiness, sleepiness, colours appear more intense, music sounds better.

Unpleasant

Around one in ten cannabis users have unpleasant experiences, including confusion, hallucinations, anxiety and paranoia. The same person may have either pleasant or unpleasant effects depending on their mood and circumstances. These feelings are usually only temporary – although as the drug can stay in the system for some weeks, the effect can be more long-lasting than users realise. Long-term use can have a depressant effect, reducing motivation.

Education and learning

There have also been suggestions that cannabis may interfere with a person's capacity to:

⇨ concentrate

⇨ organise information

⇨ use information

This effect seems to last several weeks after use, which can cause particular problems for students.

However, a large study in New Zealand followed 1,265 children for 25 years. It found that cannabis use in adolescence was linked to poor school performance, but that there was no direct connection between the two. It looked as though it was simply because cannabis use encouraged a way of life that didn't help with schoolwork.

Work

It seems to have a similar effect on people at work. There is no evidence that cannabis causes specific health hazards. But users are more likely to leave work without permission, spend work time on personal matters or simply daydream. Cannabis users themselves report that drug use has interfered with their work and social life.

Of course, some areas of work are more demanding than others. A review of the research on the effect of cannabis on pilots revealed that those who had used cannabis made far more mistakes, both major and minor, than when they had not smoked cannabis. As you can imagine, the pilots were tested in flight simulators, not actually flying... The worst effects were in the first four hours, although they persisted for at least 24 hours, even when the pilot had no sense at all of being 'high'. It concluded: 'Most of us, with this evidence, would not want to fly with a pilot who had smoked cannabis within the last day or so.'

What about driving?

In New Zealand, researchers found that those who smoked regularly, and had smoked before driving, were more likely to be injured in a car crash. A recent study in France looked at over 10,000 drivers who were involved in fatal car crashes. Even when the influence of alcohol was taken into account, cannabis users were more than twice as likely to be the cause of a fatal crash than to be one of the victims. So – perhaps most of us would also not want to be driven by somebody who had smoked cannabis in the last day or so.

Mental health problems

There is growing evidence that people with serious mental illness, including depression and psychosis, are more likely to use cannabis or have used it for long periods of time in the past. Regular use of the drug has appeared to double the risk of developing a psychotic episode or long-term schizophrenia. However, does cannabis cause depression and schizophrenia or do people with these disorders use it as a medication?

Over the past few years, research has strongly suggested that there is a clear link between early cannabis use and later mental health problems in those with a genetic vulnerability – and that there is a particular issue with the use of cannabis by adolescents.

Depression

A study following 1,600 Australian school-children, aged 14 to 15 for seven years, found that while children who use cannabis regularly have a significantly higher risk of depression, the opposite was not the case – children who already suffered from depression were not more likely than anyone else to use cannabis. However, adolescents who used cannabis daily were five times more likely to develop depression and anxiety in later life.

Schizophrenia

Three major studies followed large numbers of people over several years, and showed that those people who use cannabis have a higher than average risk of developing schizophrenia. If you start smoking it before the age of 15, you are four times more likely to develop a psychotic disorder by the time you are 26. They found no evidence of self-medication. It seemed that, the more cannabis someone used, the more likely they were to develop symptoms.

Why should teenagers be particularly vulnerable to the use of cannabis? No one knows for certain, but it may be something to do with brain development. The brain is still developing in the teenage years – up to the age of around 20, in fact. A massive process of 'neural pruning' is going on. This is rather like streamlining a tangled jumble of circuits so they can work more effectively. Any experience, or substance, that affects this process has the potential to produce long-term psychological effects.

Recent research in Europe, and in the UK, has suggested that people who have a family background of mental illness – and so probably have a genetic vulnerability anyway – are more likely to develop schizophrenia if they use cannabis as well.

Physical health problems

The main risk to physical health from cannabis is probably from the tobacco that it is often smoked with.

Is there such a thing as 'cannabis psychosis'?

Recent research in Denmark suggests that yes, there is. It is a short-lived psychotic disorder that seems to be brought on by cannabis use but which subsides fairly quickly once the individual has stopped using it. It's quite unusual though – in the whole of Denmark they found only around 100 new cases per year.

However, they also found that:

⇨ Three quarters had a different psychotic disorder diagnosed within the next year.

⇨ Nearly half still had a psychotic disorder three years later.

So, it also seems probable that nearly half of those diagnosed as having cannabis psychosis are actually showing the first signs of a more long-

lasting psychotic disorder, such as schizophrenia. It may be this group of people who are particularly vulnerable to the effects of cannabis, and so should probably avoid it in the future.

Is cannabis addictive?

It has some of the features of addictive drugs such as:

⇨ tolerance – having to take more and more to get the same effect

⇨ withdrawal symptoms. These have been shown in heavy users and include:

  ⇨ craving

  ⇨ decreased appetite

  ⇨ sleep difficulty

  ⇨ weight loss

  ⇨ aggression and/or anger

  ⇨ irritability

  ⇨ restlessness

  ⇨ strange dreams.

These symptoms of withdrawal produce about the same amount of discomfort as withdrawing from tobacco.

For regular, long-term users:

⇨ three out of four experience cravings;

⇨ half become irritable;

⇨ seven out of ten switch to tobacco in an attempt to stay off cannabis.

The irritability, anxiety and problems with sleeping usually appear ten hours after the last joint, and peak at around one week after the last use of the drug.

Compulsive use

The user feels they have to have it and spends much of their life seeking, buying and using it. They cannot stop even when other important parts of their life (family, school, work) suffer.

You are most likely to become dependent on cannabis if you use it every day.

What about skunk and other stronger varieties?

The amount of the main psycho-active ingredient, THC, that you get in herbal cannabis varies hugely from as low as 1% up to 15%. The newer strains, including skunk, can have up to 20%. The newer varieties are, on the whole, two or three times stronger than those that were available 30 years ago. It works more quickly, and can produce hallucinations with profound relaxation and elation – along with nervousness, anxiety attacks, projectile vomiting and a strong desire to eat. They may be used by some as a substitute for Ecstasy or LSD.

Legally, these strains remain classified Class B drugs. While there is little research so far, it is likely that these stronger strains carry a higher risk of causing mental illness. A major study currently underway has already reported problems with concentration and short-term memory in users of stronger types of cannabis.

Reducing cannabis use

The Home Office recently published a guide on how to cut down and stop cannabis use. It suggests a range of things you can do to successfully stop using, including:

⇨ drawing up a list of reasons for wanting to change

⇨ planning how you will change

⇨ thinking about coping with withdrawal symptoms

⇨ having a back-up plan.

If you decide to give up cannabis, it may be no more difficult than giving up cigarettes.

If you choose to go it alone there is a handy leaflet on the FRANK website.

Many people will be able to stop on their own. However, if this isn't enough:

⇨ Join a support group, for instance the online Marijuana Anonymous UK.

⇨ Talk to your GP or practice nurse. They will have a lot of experience in helping people to cut down their drinking and to stop smoking. They can also refer you to more specialist services, such as a counsellor, support group or NHS substance misuse service.

⇨ NHS substance misuse services offer assessment and counselling for a range of street drugs, aiming to help with:

- harm reduction – reducing the impact of the drug on your life
- abstinence – stopping completely
- relapse prevention – not starting to use again
- some offer a specific service for cannabis users.

Where can I get more help and information?

'Talk to Frank' is an excellent website. You can order free information leaflets for different age groups, read real-life stories of other people's experience with drugs and get reliable, factual information. Helpline: 0300 123 6600. Use the search facility to get the contact details of organisations offering practical help and support in your area.

Film Exchange on Alcohol and Drugs (FEAD): an online resource from leading figures in the alcohol and drugs field.

References

Further consideration of the classification of cannabis under the Misuse of Drugs Act 1971 (2005) Advisory Council on the Misuse of Drugs. Home Office: London.

Cannabis use and mental health in young people: cohort study (2002) George C Patton et al. British Medical Journal, 325, 1195–1198.

Cannabis and educational achievement (2003) Fergusson DM, Horwood LJ & Beautrais AL. Addiction, 98(12), 1681–1692.

Cannabinoids and the human uterus during pregnancy (2004) Dennedy MC et al. American Journal of Obstetrics and Gynaecology, 190(1), 2–9.

Bandolier: Cannabis and flying

Cannabis intoxication and fatal road crashes in France: population based case control study (2005) Laumon B et al. British Medical Journal, 331, 1371–1377.

Marijuana abstinence effects in marijuana smokers maintained in their home environment (2001) Budney AJ et al. Archives of General Psychiatry, 58, 917–924.

Marijuana use and car crash injury (2005) Blows S et al. Addiction, 100 (5), 605.

Self reported cannabis use as a risk factor for schizophrenia in Swedish conscripts of 1969: historical cohort study (2002) Zammit S, Allebeck P, Andreasson S, Lundberg I, Lewis G. British Medical Journal; 325, 1199–1201.

Cannabis use and psychosis: A longitudinal population-based study (2002) Van Os J, Bak M, Hanssen M, Bijl RV, de Graaf R, Verdoux H. American Journal of Epidemiology, 156, 319–327.

Cannabis use in adolescence and risk for adult psychosis: longitudinal prospective study (2002) Arseneault L, Cannon M, Poulton R, Murray R, Caspi A, Moffit TE. British Medical Journal, 325, 1212–1213.

Cannabis use and mental health in young people: cohort study (2002) Patton GC, Coffey C, Carlin JB, Degenhardt L, Lynskey M, Hall W. British Medical Journal; 325, 1195–1198.

A longitudinal study of cannabis use and mental health from adolescence to early adulthood (2000) McGee R, Williams S, Poulton R, Moffitt T. Addiction, 95, 491–503.

Mental health of teenagers who use cannabis (2002) Rey JM et al. British Journal of Psychiatry, 180, 216–221.

Prospective cohort study of cannabis use, predisposition for psychosis and psychotic symptoms in young people. Henquet C et al. British Medical Journal, 330, 11–14.

Tests of causal linkages between cannabis use and psychotic symptoms (2005) Fergusson DM, Horwood LJ and Ridder EM. Addiction, 100 (3), 354–366.

Cannabis-induced psychosis and subsequent schizophrenia-spectrum disorders: follow–up study of 535 incident cases (2005) Arendt M et al. British Journal of Psychiatry, 187, 510–515.

Note

The leaflet from which this article was taken, was produced by the Royal College of Psychiatrists' Public Education Editorial Board.

Series editor: Dr Philip Timms.

Expert review: Dr Eilish Gilvarry, Dr Zerin Atakan & the Addictions Faculty.

User and Carer input: Members of the RCPsych Service User Recovery Forum and Carers' Forum.

With grateful thanks to Jane Feinmann.

November 2012

⇨ The above information is reprinted with kind permission from the Royal College of Psychiatrists. Please visit www.rcpsych.ac.uk for further information.

Problems with cannabis use

Many – perhaps most – people who use cannabis do enjoy it. But it can become a problem for some people. A US organisation, marijuana–anonymous.org, defines the problems of cannabis as follows:

'If cannabis controls our lives and our thinking, and if our desires centre around marijuana – scoring it, dealing it and finding ways to stay high so that we lose interest in all else.'

The website carries the following questionnaire – which could equally well apply to alcohol use.

If you answer 'Yes' to any of the questions, you may have a problem.

1. Has smoking pot stopped being fun?

2. Do you ever get high alone?

3. Is it hard for you to imagine a life without marijuana?

4. Do you find that your friends are determined by your marijuana use?

5. Do you smoke marijuana to avoid dealing with your problems?

6. Do you smoke pot to cope with your feelings?

7. Does your marijuana use let you live in a privately defined world?

8. Have you ever failed to keep promises you made about cutting down or controlling your dope smoking?

9. Has marijuana caused problems with memory, concentration or motivation?

10. When your stash is nearly empty, do you feel anxious or worried about how to get more?

11. Do you plan your life around your marijuana use?

12. Have friends or relatives ever complained that your pot smoking is damaging your relationship with them?

November 2012

⇨ The above information is reprinted with kind permission from the Royal College of Psychiatrists. Please visit www.rcpsych.ac.uk for further information.

Characteristics of frequent and high-risk cannabis users

Cannabis is Europe's most commonly used illicit drug, with approximately 20 million adults, or around 6% of the population aged 15–64 years, having used the drug in the last year. An indication of the public health impact of the drug can be seen in the numbers entering specialised treatment in Europe for drug-related problems, among whom cannabis is the second most frequently reported drug, after heroin. Against this backdrop, identifying the characteristics of frequent and high-risk cannabis users can help with the identification and design of interventions for those cannabis users most at risk of experiencing problems.

This analysis uses two main data sources to explore frequent and high-risk cannabis use in Europe. First, general population surveys provide data on frequency of cannabis use. Secondly, data collected by specialised drug treatment centres on clients entering treatment for problems primarily related to cannabis use give insight into the personal and social characteristics of this group of users, a high proportion of which may be engaging in high-risk patterns of cannabis use. Additional information is derived from the literature.

Frequent and high-risk cannabis use in Europe: prevalence of the phenomenon

Any description of intensive forms of cannabis use is complicated by a lack of consensus on the terminology. For monitoring purposes, the EMCDDA uses 'daily or near-daily use' (use on 20 days or more in a month), which is also referred to as 'frequent cannabis use'. High-risk cannabis use is defined as 'cannabis use disorder', as described in the current international diagnostic manuals (i.e. ICD and DSM). This includes, in particular, cannabis dependence.

The most recent EMCDDA estimate suggests that there are around three million daily cannabis users in Europe (EMCDDA, 2012). Additional information can be found in youth surveys which monitor the prevalence of more intensive cannabis use (40 or more times in life) in 15- to 16-year-old school students. Prevalence of intensive use in this group ranges from 0.3% to 8%, depending on the country.

Data on users entering drug treatment for cannabis-related problems can also shed some light on high-risk cannabis use in Europe. Among clients who entered drug treatment for the first time in their life in 2011, cannabis use is the most frequently cited reason – and has been since 2008. The number of first-time cannabis clients has risen markedly, mainly since 2008. Currently, cannabis clients represent around half or more of all clients entering drug treatment in five countries (France, Denmark, Cyprus, Hungary and The Netherlands). Country differences in levels of treatment demand need to be interpreted with caution, however, and may reflect differences in treatment provision, referral practices, legislation, in addition to the prevalence of intensive cannabis use. For example, referrals from the criminal justice system may blur the picture by introducing into the treatment system cannabis users with less frequent patterns of use.

Males particularly over-represented among frequent and high-risk cannabis users

Males are generally over-represented among cannabis users, and their share in the cannabis-using population has what is known as a 'dose-dependent relationship' with frequency of use and related problems. This means that the proportion of males increases with frequency of cannabis use, and is highest among those with problems related to cannabis (here represented by users entering treatment). So, while approximately 70% of last year cannabis users are male, the proportion of males rises to 75% among last month users, 78% among daily users in the last month and 84% among treatment entrants reporting cannabis as their primary drug (see Table 1). Over-representation of males among users is typical for illicit drugs; however, cannabis clients present one of the highest ratios of males to females among drug clients entering treatment. Although there is some variation between countries, all report that three-quarters or more of cannabis treatment entrants are male.

The literature highlights a number of important issues for women with daily or dependent cannabis use: for example, these women are significantly more likely to have a cannabis-using partner, but less likely to have a heavy cannabis-using social network. With similar patterns of cannabis use, they have greater concern about their cannabis use and perceived difficulty of quitting (Copeland et al., 2001; Swift et al., 2000). Males with similar patterns of use, in contrast, tend to have higher levels of alcohol and tobacco use, more criminal convictions and higher levels of psychosocial distress (Copeland et al., 2001).

Cannabis clients among the youngest in treatment

Frequent and high-risk cannabis users tend to be young people

Table 1: Gender breakdown according to frequency of cannabis use among adults (15–64 years) and treatment entrants reporting cannabis as their primary drug				
	Use of cannabis at least once in the last year	Use of cannabis at least once in the last month	Daily cannabis users	Cannabis users entering treatment (1)
Male	70%	75%	78%	84%
Female	30%	25%	22%	16%

(1) Age range among treatment entrants might be slightly broader than 15–64 years.
Source: EMCDDA Statistical Bulletin, 2013

(below 35 years of age). Of the estimated three million European daily cannabis users, roughly 70% are aged between 15 and 34, and over 86% of clients entering treatment in Europe with cannabis as their primary drug are aged 34 or less. The estimated mean age of clients entering treatment for cannabis use is 25 years, which is one of the lowest mean ages among the different groups of drug clients.

Populations of older cannabis users do exist. Studies available on users who have been using the drug for ten or more years (on average 19) suggest that they may have established a routine of cannabis use that is less intensive than that of younger frequent users. Various reasons are suggested to explain why older users may feel less inclined to discontinue their cannabis smoking: for example, they may perceive more benefits than risks from their use or experience less social pressure to stop (Korf et al., 2007; Reilly et al., 1998). As a consequence, this group may be less likely to contact services, even though problems such as cannabis dependence are not uncommon among these users (Swift et al., 2000).

The majority of frequent cannabis users will have started to use the drug while they were in their teens. The age at first use is negatively related to the level of harm potentially experienced by the user. Early initiation and regular cannabis use during adolescence have been found to be associated with numerous negative outcomes, including problematic patterns of cannabis use, use of other illicit drugs, mental health problems

and low educational achievement (Copeland and Swift, 2009; Fischer et al., 2011). It is important not to infer that early cannabis use causes all the above-mentioned harms, as there are numerous common and overlapping risk factors and life experiences that may explain this association.

Socio-economic status: diverse findings

Data on the socio-economic status of frequent cannabis users are scarce and sometimes contradictory. A recent Dutch study (van der Pol et al., 2013) found frequent cannabis users to have, on average, a higher level of educational attainment than the general population; however, they were more often unemployed or unable to work. In two Australian studies (Copeland et al., 2001; Reilly et al., 1998), community samples of heavy or long-term cannabis users had levels of educational attainment and employment similar to or higher than those of the general population. A 2012 analysis of EU treatment demand data found that most cannabis users entering treatment were living in stable accommodation (60–90%). Depending on the country, somewhere between one-third and two-thirds had completed at least secondary education, while between 40% and 60% were in full-time education or employment. Unemployment among primary cannabis users entering treatment ranged from 7% to 40%.

A recent study among French adolescents supports the view that

higher socio-economic status has a protective effect against daily cannabis use (Legleye et al., 2011). Findings suggest that although young people from families with higher socio-economic status had higher risk of experimental use of cannabis, they were also less likely to engage in daily use of the drug.

Conclusions

This exploration of the evidence on the characteristics of frequent cannabis users supports the findings of studies which identify young males as a population group that is over-represented among frequent cannabis users. Among frequent and daily users of cannabis, dependence is a concern and may help to explain some of the variation that exists in patterns of use, mental health and cannabis-related problems. With regard to the design of appropriate interventions for users most at risk of experiencing problems, evidence presented here suggests that these should be suited to predominantly young male populations with high levels of cannabis-related problems, poly-drug use patterns and likely mental health problems. Treatment options should take into account the significant minority of women among those with cannabis problems, as they may have different needs. Looking towards the future, treatment services may see growing numbers of older cannabis users, if a sizeable proportion of the current relatively large population of frequent cannabis users continue to use the drug intensively as they age.

Facts and figures

- 20 million have used the drug in the last year.

- 11 million have used cannabis in the last month.

- Three million have used the drug daily or almost daily in the last month.

- More than three-quarters of all reported drug law offences in the European Union are related to cannabis, and this figure has been increasing since 2006.

- In about two-thirds of the EU Member States, the cannabis market is dominated by herbal cannabis; cannabis resin dominates in the other Member States.

- The typical (modal) potency and price of cannabis 'products' varies widely among EU Member States, with potency (%THC) ranging from approximately 1% to 15%, and price from EUR 5 to EUR 15 per gram.

- Cannabis use can cause adverse health effects, both acute and chronic. Of the acute effects, an increased risk of being involved in motor vehicle accidents is one of the most serious consequences. Chronic effects include dependence, respiratory diseases and psychotic symptoms. Risks to health generally increase with early onset and increasing frequency of use and quantity used.

- Cannabis dependence is usually diagnosed in Europe according to the World Health Organization's *International Classification of Diseases*, 10th revision. It can be described as 'a cluster of behavioural, cognitive and physiological phenomena that develop after repeated substance use and that typically include a strong desire to take the drug, difficulties in controlling its use, persisting in its use despite harmful consequences, a higher priority given to drug use than to other activities and obligations, increased tolerance and sometimes a physical withdrawal state'.

References

Copeland, J. and Swift, W. (2009), 'Cannabis use disorder: Epidemiology and management', *International Review of Psychiatry* 21, pp. 96–103.

Copeland, J., Swift, W. and Rees, V. (2001), 'Clinical profile of participants in a brief intervention program for cannabis use disorder', *Journal of Substance Abuse Treatment* 20, pp. 45–52.

European Monitoring Centre for Drugs and Drug Addiction (EMCDDA) (2012), Prevalence of daily cannabis use in the European Union and Norway (available online).

Fischer, B., Jeffries, V., Hall, W., Room, R., Goldner, E. and Rehm, J. (2011), 'Lower risk cannabis use guidelines for Canada (LRCUG): a narrative review of evidence and recommendations', *Revue Canadienne de Santé Publique* 102, pp. 324–327.

Korf, D. J., Benschol, A. and Wouters, M. (2007), 'Differential responses to cannabis potency: A typology of users based on self-reported consumption behaviour', *International Journal of Drug Policy* 18, pp. 168–176.

Legleye, S., Janssen, E., Beck, F., Chau, N. and Khlat, M. (2011), 'Social gradient in initiation and transition to daily use of tobacco and cannabis during adolescence: a retrospective cohort study', *Addiction* 106, pp. 1520–1531.

Reilly, D., Didicott, P., Swift, W. and Hall, W. (1998), 'Long-term cannabis use: characteristics of users in an Australian rural area', *Addiction* 93, pp. 837–846.

Swift, W., Hall, W. and Copeland, J. (2000), 'One year follow-up of cannabis dependence among long-term users in Sydney, Australia', *Drug and Alcohol Dependence* 59, pp. 309–318.

Van der Pol, P., Liebregts, N., de Graaf, R., ten Have, M., Korf, D. J., van den Brink, W. and van Laar, M. (2013), 'Mental health differences between frequent cannabis users with and without cannabis dependence and the general population', *Addiction* 108, pp. 1459–1469.

⇨ The above information is reprinted with kind permission from EMCDDA. Please visit www.emcdda.europa.eu for further information.

© EMCDDA 2013

Does cannabis help people beat drug dependency?

By Paul Bramhall

Drug policy around the world is focused on preventing people from becoming drug dependent. But given that some people do become drug dependent, what can we do to help them? Over the years many ideas for effectively beating drug dependency have come forward, from the obscure drug ibogaine to firing lasers into the brain. One simple idea is slowly gaining currency: cannabis as a substitute drug for other substances considered more harmful.

In 2012 a research team surveyed the customers of four medical marijuana dispensaries in British Columbia, Canada. Three quarters of them said they substitute cannabis for at least one other substance. 41% of them substitute it for alcohol, 36% for illicit substances and 68% for prescription drugs. The three main reasons people gave were less withdrawal, fewer side-effects and better symptom management.

A 2006 study by the New York State Psychiatric Institute found that cannabis users were more successful than other patients in abstaining from cocaine use. And a 1999 study in Brazil found that 68% of subjects who self-medicated with cannabis in order to reduce cravings were able to give up crack altogether.

But why would cannabis help beat drug dependency? The craving and impulsiveness of drug dependency is associated with low levels of serotonin, a chemical found in the brain. Cannabinoids such as THC are seratoninenergic agonists, which means they can activate serotonin receptors on brain cells, thereby mimicking the effects of serotonin. In this way, cannabis can reduce craving and impulsiveness.

In addition, people who have participated in studies have suggested that the ritual of rolling a joint helps to reduce the habituated psychological

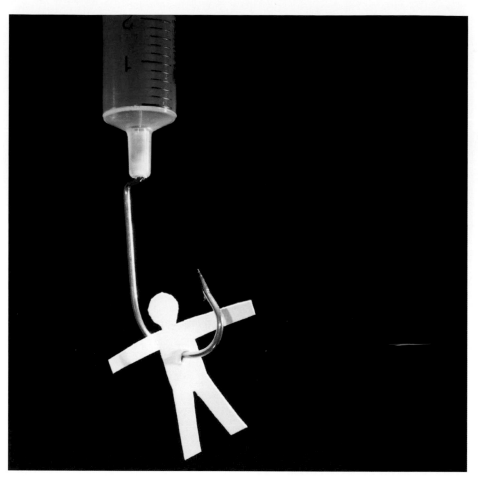

dependence associated with the preparation of crack cocaine.

Bogota, the capital of Colombia, will soon be opening 'controlled consumption centres', where drug-dependent people can consume in a safe environment, with the goal of kicking the habit. They will bravely test out the theory that cannabis is a good substitute. Julián Quintero, from the charity Acción Técnica Social, explains how it will work: 'The first thing you do is to start to reduce the dose. After that, you begin to change the way that it's administered: if you were injecting heroin, you move to smoking heroin; after smoking heroin, you move to combining it with cannabis; after that, you're staying with the cannabis. After that there's a good chance of them becoming functional again.'

The Canadian research team concludes their report by saying, 'Given the credible biological, social and psychological mechanisms behind these results, and the associated potential to decrease personal suffering and the personal and social costs associated with addiction, further research appears to be justified on both economic and ethical grounds.' Cannabis has for many years been accused of being a gateway drug. However it seems that it would be much more accurate to call it an exit drug.

22 April 2013

⇨ The above information is reprinted with kind permission from TalkingDrugs. Please visit www.talkingdrugs.org for further information.

Cannabis and MS

Say the name cannabis and universally, people think 'drugs'! Illegal, mind bending, out of control, irresponsible and just plain bad substance misuse are also some phrases that may go along with this thought!

However, plants have played a part in healing for many centuries and *cannabis sativa* is one of those to rank with the oldest to attract medicinal interest. Cannabis is sometimes called 'marijuana', but this is actually the name of the dried leaves of the plant, whereas 'hashish' refers to blocks of resin. Over 60 cannabinoids (CB) have been found contained in the plant, with different biological activity.

In the 1960s, an Israeli scientist called Raphael Mechoulam discovered the plant's active molecules, which he called cannabinoids. This led to the discovery of the body's own cannabinoid system, which is important in many organs, including the brain.

Pain is a significant feature of MS. Several trials have confirmed that cannabis-based treatments alleviate MS-related neuropathic pain. Surveys of people with MS who smoke cannabis often report a reduction in muscle stiffness (spasticity). The hope that cannabis may help MS has led to numerous clinical trials, but response in MS can be difficult to evaluate and reliable studies require large numbers of subjects and careful planning.

Possible benefits

⇨ Relieves pain

⇨ Relieves spasms and spasticity

⇨ Improves bladder and bowel control

⇨ May improve eyesight and restore feeling to nerve endings.

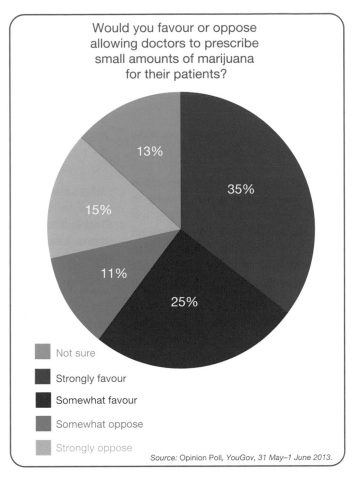

Would you favour or oppose allowing doctors to prescribe small amounts of marijuana for their patients?

- 13%
- 35%
- 15%
- 11%
- 25%

Not sure
Strongly favour
Somewhat favour
Somewhat oppose
Strongly oppose

Source: Opinion Poll, YouGov, 31 May–1 June 2013.

Possible risks

⇨ Anxiety, psychosis and panic attacks

⇨ Loss of concentration and impaired memory may cause brain shrinkage.

Did you know?

⇨ Canada is the first country to legalise the possession of cannabis for people with chronic illness.

⇨ Belgium is the second country (after Holland) to have decriminalised the use of cannabis though not its sale. The Government in Belgium sees no reason why it should be treated differently to alcohol or tobacco.

⇨ Two states in the US have approved measures to legalise the non-medical use of cannabis, whereas 18 other US states have passed laws allowing some degree of medical use of marijuana.

⇨ The above information is reprinted with kind permission from MS-UK. Please visit www.ms-uk.org for further information.

© MS-UK 2013

Does smoking 'dope' turn you into one?

' Adolescents who are regular users of cannabis are at risk of permanent damage to their intelligence, attention span and memory,' reported *The Guardian*.

The news was based on an impressive and wide-ranging study of 1,037 New Zealanders who were followed from birth up to the age of 38.

Researchers aimed to investigate the association between persistent cannabis use and mental function over a 20-year period, and to see whether greater decline was seen among those who started using cannabis in their teens. They found that those who did and then carried on using cannabis into later life experienced a small drop in IQ of a few points. They also scored less than non-cannabis smokers in other tests of mental function, such as mental arithmetic.

Interestingly, other studies have not found a similar drop in IQ or mental function in people who begin smoking cannabis as an adult. One possible theory to explain this is smoking cannabis as a teen could disrupt the development of the brain (the brain is not fully developed until around the age of 18). This in turn could lead to corresponding problems with mental functions. Further research is required to confirm or disprove this theory.

While the evidence is compelling, as the researchers admit, there is still not enough of it to show a clear direct cause and effect between teenage cannabis smoking and reduced intelligence. The possible observed link could be due to other unmeasured factors (for example, other mental health issues).

Where did the story come from?

The study was carried out by researchers from the University of Otago in New Zealand, Duke University in the US, the King's College in London and other institutions. It was supported by the New Zealand Health Research Council, the UK Medical Research Council, the US National Institute on Aging, the US National Institute of Mental Health and the US Institute on Drug and Abuse.

The study was published in the peer-reviewed journal *PNAS (Proceedings of the National Academy of Sciences)*.

The story was covered appropriately by BBC News and picked up by a variety of other papers and online media.

What kind of research was this?

This was a prospective cohort study looking at the effects of cannabis use on IQ in New Zealand.

Cohort studies are useful for looking at possible associations between various lifestyle factors (such as smoking cannabis) and health outcomes (such as

a person's neuropsychological development). They enable researchers to follow large groups of people for many years but they cannot establish cause and effect.

A prospective study recruits appropriate participants and looks at the exposures or provides treatments, and then measures outcomes of interest in these people over the following months or years.

Results from prospective studies are usually considered more robust then retrospective studies, which either use data collected in the past for another purpose, or ask participants to remember what has happened to them in the past.

The difficulty with a cohort study such as this, is that it cannot take into account all the possible factors that could be related to both cannabis use and mental functioning. So there may be other factors that are missed by the researchers – as the paper states – 'there may be some unknown "third" variable that could account for these findings'.

What did the research involve?

Researchers recruited 1,037 individuals from the larger Dunedin Multidisciplinary Health and Development Study in New Zealand that was investigating the long-term health and behaviours of participants. The study participants were followed from their birth in 1972/1973 up until the age of 38.

Cannabis dependence was determined using recognised criteria in interviews at five different ages:

⇨ 18 years – people at this point were also asked about any earlier history of cannabis use

⇨ 21 years

⇨ 26 years

⇨ 32 years

⇨ 38 years.

Cannabis dependence is normally defined as:

⇨ experiencing withdrawal symptoms if the supply of cannabis is withdrawn, or conversely, smoking cannabis to avoid these symptoms

⇨ being unable to control or cut down the amount of cannabis that you smoke

⇨ developing an increasing tolerance to the effects of cannabis.

In assessing persistent cannabis use, participants were grouped as those who:

⇨ never used cannabis

⇨ used cannabis but not regularly

- used cannabis regularly at one of the age-assessment points

- used cannabis regularly at two of the age-assessment points.

- used cannabis regularly at three or more age assessment points (this was considered as persistent cannabis dependence).

To determine neuropsychological functioning, intelligence was assessed using various IQ tests in childhood at ages 7, 9, 11 and 13 and again in adulthood at age 38.

As well as the standard IQ test, other tests of mental functioning were also carried out, including:

- mental arithmetic

- vocabulary testing

- block design test (where people are asked to assemble coloured blocks into a set pattern).

At the 38-year mark, participants also nominated a person who knew them well (who the researchers called informants).

These informants were asked to fill out questionnaires about the person's mental functioning including any attention and memory problems.

The researchers then looked at changes in IQ from childhood to adulthood to see if cannabis had an effect on any changes seen.

The researchers analysed their results using statistical methods and took into account other factors that could account for the decline in mental functioning such as:

- alcohol and tobacco dependence

- other drug use (for example, heroin, cocaine and amphetamines)

- a diagnosis of schizophrenia

- number of years spent in education.

What were the basic results?

The main findings from this study were:

- Participants who reported more persistent cannabis use showed greater neuropsychological decline. For example, those who reported never using cannabis showed a slight increase in IQ, whereas those considered cannabis dependent at one, two or three of the age-assessment points, showed declines in IQ.

- Participants with more persistent cannabis dependence generally had greater neuropsychological impairment.

- IQ impairment was more pronounced among those who used cannabis in adolescence, with more persistent use associated with greater IQ decline.

- Adolescent cannabis users (infrequent and frequent use), who stopped using cannabis for one year or more, did not fully restore their neuropsychological functioning at 38 years, whereas participants who were frequent or infrequent cannabis users in adulthood did.

How did the researchers interpret the results?

The researchers conclude that persistent cannabis use over 20 years is associated with neuropsychological decline and that greater decline is seen among those who are more persistent cannabis users.

They say this effect was most evident among those who take up cannabis use while in adolescence. The researchers theorised that this could be the result of persistent cannabis use during teenage years disrupting the development of the brain.

In discussing their research findings the authors say that, 'prevention and policy efforts should focus on delivering to the public the message that cannabis use during adolescence can have harmful effects on neuropsychological functioning'.

They went on to add that a useful harm reduction message arising from the research was that (to paraphrase), 'ideally people should avoid smoking cannabis, but if they are determined to do so, at least wait until adulthood'.

Teenagers who are currently smoking cannabis should be encouraged to quit.

Conclusion

Overall, this study provided some evidence to support the growing literature on the potential harm of cannabis, particularly among adolescents.

The most important limitation is that, despite the author's efforts to adjust for confounders, it is always possible that other factors (for example, socioeconomic factors or other unmeasured mental health issues) influenced the results and were underlying the apparent association. It is important to note that this research does not prove that there is a direct causal link (that is, teenage cannabis use leads to an IQ decline) only that there is an association.

It's also worth noting that this research undertook extensive statistical calculations to look at the relationship between different measures of IQ and different durations of cannabis use, some of which involved only small sample sizes. For example, despite the large initial sample size (1,037), only 41 people (3.95% of the people surveyed) used cannabis regularly at all three time points. Calculations based on such small sample size decreases the reliability of these risk associations.

Another issue is whether cannabis use was accurately recorded. Interestingly only seven participants reported trying cannabis by age 13, and cannabis

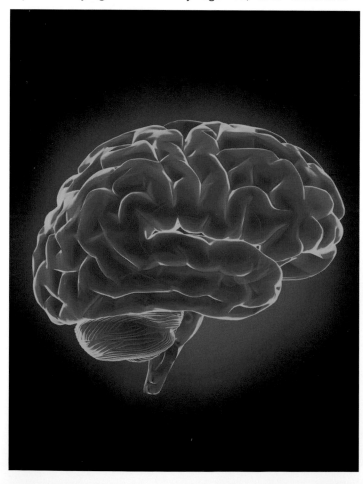

use during adolescence was only accounted for in the assessment at 18 years where participants were asked about use in the previous year, that is, while they were 17. It is also possible that participants did not accurately report their cannabis use patterns in the year before each of the assessments, which can make the results less reliable.

The fact that informants were also asked to assess participants on things such as memory and attention span may also make the results somewhat unreliable as people's personal opinions are by definition highly subjective.

Validation of cannabis use using laboratory measures would have made the results more reliable. However, persuading 'dope-smoking 20-somethings' to attend regular blood tests may be somewhat challenging.

Another factor is that the potency of the cannabis smoked was not reported. There has been a growing trend of people smoking stronger strains of cannabis (such as skunk) over the course of the last few decades.

So if there is a dose-dependent effect between cannabis use and IQ impairment then the effect in today's teenagers could be even more pronounced.

The researchers note that further research is needed on the effects of the quantity, frequency and the age-of-onset of cannabis use on neuropsychological impairment.

The full longer effects of cannabis use are not completely known, but in the shorter term cannabis can cause variable psychological effects, which may differ extensively between individuals.

Despite these limitations this is a useful piece of research that adds to a growing body of work that suggests persistent cannabis use at a young age can have a negative impact on mental health and mental functioning.

Analysis by NHS Choices.

Overall this study provided some evidence to support the growing literature on the potential harm of cannabis, particularly among adolescents. As one researcher was quoted saying: 'Cannabis... is risky for under-18 brains'.

28 August 2012

⇨ The above information is reprinted with kind permission from NHS Choices. Please visit www. nhs.uk for further information.

The sloppy journalism that misrepresents cannabis use

Public knowledge of the effects of drugs and drug policy is often ill-served by the more reactionary voices in the media, but Friday 5 April 2013 was a particularly dark day.

By Ewan Hoyle

The following headlines splashed across *The Mail*: 'The price of going soft on cannabis: Labour's experiment "pushed up hard drug use and crime"', and *The Telegraph*: 'Cannabis use soared by a quarter after Class C downgrade, study finds', and ''Softly softly' cannabis scheme drove up hospital admissions for hard drugs, study'.

Yet if you scratch below the surface of these articles – and make the effort to read the research being reported – it quickly becomes clear that the debate is being dramatically distorted by a perfect storm of shaky or incomplete research, and sensationalist reporting.

The rebuttal of 'Cannabis use soared by a quarter' is a simple one. The study which led to this misunderstanding looked at the result of the downgrading of cannabis from Class B to Class C, investigating whether there were changes in cannabis consumption as a result, and whether cannabis use was associated with other criminality and use of other drugs. One of the paper's authors, Dr. Nils Braakmann, issued a rather withering statement. It's not greatly enlightening as to what his

research did actually discover, but I shall paraphrase it thus: 'This reporting was plain wrong. How could you not know the difference between absolute and relative increases in cannabis consumption? I haven't finished my research yet. I'll call you when I do.'

The evidence up until now has indicated that reclassifying cannabis didn't seem to affect use levels at all. What Dr. Braakmann's research will contribute to the evidence base remains to be seen. Perhaps he – understandably – hadn't prepared his findings for an audience of layperson reporters, but that doesn't mean we can forgive *The Telegraph* reporter for interpreting his findings as a sensational headline with no basis in fact.

One thing that is clear from reading the paper is that they found no evidence of the 'gateway theory' that use of cannabis would lead to use of other 'harder' drugs. This is of course problematic for *The Daily Mail*'s combined reporting of the two research studies proclaiming 'Labour's experiment pushed up hard drug use'. It should also cause the authors of the second referenced study to take a long, hard look at themselves.

The second study referenced in the newspapers looked into the 2001 experiment in Lambeth during which police were instructed to stop arresting individuals for simple cannabis possession offences. Ironically perhaps, the experiment started as a response to public demand for a greater police focus on drugs like heroin and crack. In the abstract of the paper is the following sentence: 'We find the depenalisation of cannabis had significant longer term impacts on hospital admissions related to the use of hard drugs.' There is no attempt to acknowledge that the association between depenalisation and hospital admissions may be coincidental or due to other factors 'confounding variables' (the old 'correlation, not causation' chestnut), and there is no hint of any attempt to gain an understanding of the changing face of drug use and service provision within London and Lambeth at the time.

Perhaps due to an absence of expert peer review, the authors have failed to recognise the importance of the serious escalation in crack use in London that helped create the demand for the Lambeth experiment in the first place. They have also failed to see how it would have been better practice to compare Lambeth's hospital admission rates with those of boroughs with similar drug use issues rather than a London-wide average. To include leafy boroughs like Richmond and Bromley in their comparisons was completely inappropriate.

But most importantly, had they talked to any Lambeth drug workers, they might have discovered a far more plausible reason for an escalation in hospital admissions in the borough related to hard drug use.

In the year of the Lambeth cannabis experiment, a needle exchange programme called Mainliners was also set up in the borough. One of the main priorities of the programme was to encourage hard drug users to go to hospital for treatment for their serious health conditions.

So rather than the take home message of this research being: '"softly softly" cannabis scheme drove up hospital admissions for hard drugs', perhaps the headline should have been: 'needle exchange programme does fantastic job of engaging marginalised drug users with health services'.

If the headline was to be extended to include reference to the cannabis depenalisation experiment and its effects upon crime in Lambeth it perhaps should read: '...and "softly softly" approach to cannabis led to reductions in other crimes and improved arrest and clear-up rates'. These were the conclusions of another research article that was cited by both of the studies reported on Friday. As expected, regarding cannabis possession as a non-priority allowed the police to spend more time and achieve better results in addressing other criminal activity.

If a media outlet is determined to portray a policy in a bad light it is all too easy to cherry pick poor outcomes (real or not) and ignore the positives. Few readers will be any wiser.

The debate has in fact moved on in the last ten years. The question is not now whether we enforce the cannabis laws, but whether we fully legalise, regulate it and sell it on the high street. Arguably more relevant is the experience of licensed and regulated cannabis 'coffee shops' in The Netherlands. This system has taken cannabis out of the hands of street dealers who might seek to supply other 'harder' drugs, dramatically weakening the link between cannabis use and the use of these drugs.

In fact, the Braakmann paper also hints at yet more advantages to legalising and regulating cannabis. Whilst they didn't find that cannabis was a 'gateway drug', there were suggestions in their findings that it might be a 'gateway crime' (my terminology). In their conclusion they state that for some users: 'those coming from "troubled" backgrounds ... cannabis consumption has adverse effects, in the sense of reinforcing pre-existing bad behaviour.'

Is it possible that the act of committing a crime in using cannabis reinforces an identity of outlaw and delinquent in young people, making it more like for them to develop other antisocial behaviours? If so, is this an argument against cannabis use or an argument against its illegality? Would legalising cannabis lead to a more sensible alignment of moral and criminal boundaries? Would it cause it to be harder for young people to break through those boundaries and be 'bad' in the eyes of society and when they look at themselves in the mirror? I think on balance it would.

Who knew that behind those headlines we'd find yet more reasons to legalise and regulate the cannabis market, and possible evidence of a very successful harm reduction service? These may in fact prove useful lessons for the future, but the larger message of this episode is to remind us how bad science and politicisation of drug policy reporting has been a key factor in maintaining the failed policies of prohibition.

Ewan Hoyle is the founder of Liberal Democrats for Drug Policy Reform.

The opinions in Politics.co.uk's Comment and Analysis section are those of the author and are no reflection of the views of the website or its owners.

7 April 2013

⇨ The above information is reprinted with kind permission from Politics.co.uk. Please visit www. politics.co.uk for further information.

Cannabis laws

Global laws

The laws regarding cannabis vary widely from country to country. Some governments have an all-out ban on any cannabis use while others allow medical cannabis. Some have decriminalised small amounts while others allow free and legal use of cannabis. There are even a few countries that will condemn cannabis users to death. This makes it incredibly important to know and understand the laws before you travel and understand that cannabis law is an ever changing tapestry.

UK laws

In the UK it is illegal to sell, possess, grow or distribute cannabis without a licence. Cannabis is considered a class B drug which means possession carries a sentence of up to five years in prison or an unlimited fine, or both. For those caught dealing cannabis, there is a prison term of up to 14 years and an unlimited fine, or both.

What if I am caught with cannabis?

If you are caught with a small amount of drugs you can be charged with possession of an illegal substance. The police can take the drugs from you and arrest you on the spot. If you are under 18 they can also notify your parents.

Usually police will issue a cannabis warning for first-time offenders who are over 18. For those under 18 with no previous record, police often give a reprimand and contact a parent. Keep in mind police are more likely to make an arrest if you are smoking in a public place with little regard for getting caught.

What if I am caught with cannabis for a second or third time?

If you are caught with cannabis three times, police will most likely arrest you. This means the courts will be involved and you could receive up to five years in prison and an unlimited fine.

What If I am caught dealing cannabis?

If you are caught dealing or supplying cannabis, police are likely to deal more harshly with you. The police will most likely charge you and then the courts can issue either/or a fine, jail time or other punishment they see fit. It is important to remember that simply sharing drugs is considered supplying them so sharing a cannabis joint could technically be considered supplying.

For those caught supplying, there is a maximum 14-year prison sentence and an unlimited fine.

Can I own cannabis seeds?

It is completely legal to own cannabis seeds in the UK. They are often used in birdseed and fishing bait. These seeds can be legal but as soon as they are grown into a cannabis plant, it becomes illegal.

Can I get a prescription for cannabis?

You cannot get a prescription for cannabis in the UK. The Government does not recognise cannabis as a medical product and they say it has too many negative side effects to be used safely. The Government have no plans to change this.

More cannabis information

Between 2004 and 2009 cannabis was reclassified as a class C drug as a way to reduce the number of people in prison for possession and focus on distribution. The reclassification of cannabis as a class B drug came in January 2009 after political outcry. There was also some concern over new research around psychosis but there is no definitive study proving or disproving this.

By classifying cannabis as class B, the UK Government has placed it among drugs like amphetamines (cocaine), Methylphenidate (Ritalin) and Pholcodine. All of these can have dramatic effects on the body and have at least some risk of addiction.

More recently, the House of Commons weighed in on cannabis. In 2012 the Home Affairs Select Committee produced a report on UK drug policies. The report

recommended reclassification of cannabis back to class C.

According to the UK Home Office young people in possession of cannabis will be arrested and taken to a police station. From there, they will receive a reprimand, final warning or charge based on the seriousness of the offence.

After a reprimand, any offence by a young person will lead to a final warning. After that any offence usually results in criminal charges. The offender will also be referred to a Youth Offending Team to arrange a rehabilitation programme.

For adults, anyone who is caught with cannabis can be arrested. Police also have the power to issue a warning which is used mostly for first-time offenders. They can also issue a penalty notice for disorder. This includes an on-the-spot fine of £80.

Sources:

Gov.UK, Wikipedia, Talk To Frank.

Irish laws

Irish law does not recognise cannabis as having any medical benefits. As such, their laws state that all cannabis and any cannabis derivatives are Schedule 1 drugs. This means the manufacture, production, preparation, sale, supply, distribution and possession of cannabis is illegal for any reason unless the person has a licence from the Ministry of Health. These licences are usually only granted for research, or as an essential part of a manufacturing process.

The Irish police enforcing cannabis laws have some leeway when it comes to prosecuting people using cannabis. Any cannabis found has to be seized but before the police can obtain a conviction, the cannabis must be sent to a lab for analysis. The time and money required means that police may choose not to prosecute small-time offenders. In cases like this, the cannabis is seized and the police take the name of the person in possession but often no formal charges are filed.

If the police do decide to file charges, there is a variety of penalties that can be imposed. For first-time offenders, there is a maximum fine of €381 for a summary conviction or a maximum €635 fine for a conviction on indictment.

For a second offence, the maximum fine for summary conviction goes up to €508 or €1,269 for a conviction on indictment.

The third or subsequent offence can include jail time. For summary convictions, the maximum fine is €1,269 and/or jail time for up to one year. For convictions on indictment the fine is at the court's discretion and the maximum jail time is three years.

Currently, the only cannabis-related product not totally illegal are cannabis seeds. As soon as the seeds are cultivated though, the cannabis becomes illegal.

US laws

In the US federal law bans all sales and possession of cannabis. This means it is illegal to own or sell it to anyone for any reason. The US Federal Government also technically allows the death penalty to be used in certain drug cases. These include cases where there are more than 60,000 kilograms or 60,000 plants of cannabis. It also includes criminal enterprises where people smuggle cannabis or other contraband worth over $20 million. The US Supreme Court has counteracted this though, saying that only murder and treason can be punishable by death.

While this makes it technically illegal for anyone in the US to use cannabis, individual states have started making their own laws regarding cannabis. Currently, Washington and Colorado have legalised all uses of cannabis and have begun to implement laws that would regulate cannabis in the same manner used to regulate alcohol. Including Washington and Colorado, there are currently 14 states that have some form of decriminalisation laws on the books or are taking steps towards decriminalisation. Currently, some of these states only allow use of cannabis for medical reasons while others, like Alaska, allow for small quantities of cannabis to be used recreationally in the home.

So far there has been no test case brought before the supreme court that has established whether or not states or the Federal Government have the right to control marijuana. Until this has happened, cannabis will remain in a sort of limbo, legal according to state law but still considered totally illegal by federal standards.

There are also several states that allow people to grow cannabis with low THC content for non-drug use. Vermont and North Dakota both have laws that provide hemp licensing. These states are waiting for permission from the DEA to begin issuing these licences but in the meantime, North Dakota is taking legal measures to force the DEA into approving the licenses.

Oregon already has a cannabis licensing scheme in place to grow industrial hemp but as the hemp is marked as a controlled substance, any growers are still in a legal grey area.

Many other states have legalised growing hemp but DEA resistance has prevented anyone from actually growing any yet.

Canadian laws

Currently the status of cannabis in Canada is being disputed. Superior and appellate courts in Ontario have ruled Canada's cannabis laws have no force or effect on numerous occasions but this has not resulted in changes to federal laws on cannabis. Outside of Ontario, police and prosecutors still take action against people using or distributing cannabis.

It is also illegal to grow cannabis for any reason other than medical usage despite several polls suggesting a majority of Canadians support legalisation or decriminalisation.

Canada does allow cannabis for medical use but only under certain conditions. According to the regulations established by Health Canada in July 2001, patients can be prescribed cannabis if they have severe pain and/or persistent muscle spasms from multiple sclerosis, from a spinal cord injury, from spinal cord disease, severe pain, cachexia, anorexia, weight loss, and/or severe nausea from cancer or HIV/AIDS infection, severe pain from severe forms of arthritis, or seizures from epilepsy. Cannabis is also legal for people not covered under the previous conditions if they have a debilitating medical symptoms or a medical condition and have the backing of a medical professional. Basically that means people who can justify their need for cannabis due to a medical condition and with the support of a doctor are allowed to use it.

Canada also hosts cannabis refugees who are people charged with cannabis-related crimes that have fled the US.

Australian laws

There are no national laws that deal with cannabis-related offences. Each state and territory enacts their own laws. In some jurisdictions there are criminal penalties enforced for possession, use and supply. In other areas there are civil penalties for minor offences involving cannabis. Currently, all territories and states have implemented a policy of leniency where non-violent minor or first time offences avoid the legal system. These people are often given a caution rather than facing legal penalties.

People convicted of dealing, violent crimes involving cannabis, or import or export of the drug are treated much differently.

Both import and export are highly illegal and can result in federal penalties. This can mean up to life in prison for anyone trying to import or export more than 100 kg of cannabis.

Any other violent offence involving cannabis or possession of large amounts of the drug is also likely to result in hefty fines and jail time. But again, the sentencing for this varies between different states and territories.

New Zealand laws

It is illegal to posses any amount of cannabis according to New Zealand law. If caught, even the smallest amount of cannabis could result in a fine of $500 or a three month prison sentence. Currently cannabis is a class C drug in New Zealand and those caught with more than at least 28 grams or more than 100 cannabis joints are presumed to be suppliers or dealers. If someone is found to be a supplier or dealer, they could face up to eight years in prison.

Unlike recreational use, medical cannabis is legally available in New Zealand. While it is technically legal, actually securing a prescription can be difficult. Each applicant must meet strict criteria and over the last four years, only about 30 people have been granted permission to use medical cannabis.

Jamaican laws

Cannabis is currently illegal in Jamaica but there is a growing movement pushing for legalisation. Despite being illegal, actual enforcement is rare and the drug is widely used.

⇨ The above information is reprinted with kind permission from Cannabis Dependency. Please visit www. cannabisdependency.co.uk for further information.

© Cannabis Dependency 2013

The long and winding road to cannabis legalisation

In many Western countries, between one quarter and one third of the population admit to having used cannabis at least once in their lives – according to the official statistics. This column provides an in-depth review of existing economic, social and media evidence for and against legalisation. It concludes that although there is of course uncertainty surrounding the long-term implications, prohibition is not working and it is time to legalise.

Although some countries have quasi-legalised cannabis use (The Netherlands), made cannabis available for medical purposes (California, in the US) or allowed the growing of a small number of cannabis plants for personal use (Australia), in most countries – The Netherlands included – cannabis supply, distribution and use is prohibited (Reuter, 2010). Nevertheless, in 2009, between 2.8% and 4.5% of the world population aged 15–64, corresponding to between 125 million and 203 million people had used cannabis at least once in the past year (United Nations Office on Drugs and Crime 2011).

The table opposite presents cannabis use statistics for a number of countries, distinguishing between lifetime use (ever), recent use (last year) and current use (last month). The range in lifetime use is substantial from a low 21% in Sweden to a high 42% in the United States. The range in recent cannabis use is also substantial from a low 1% in Sweden to a high 14% in Italy. Finally, current use ranges from 1% in Sweden to 7% in Spain and the United States. What is also striking is the big difference between lifetime use and recent use. In The Netherlands for example, 25% of the population aged 15 to 64 have ever used cannabis but only 7% has done so in the last year. Apparently, for a substantial part of the users, cannabis is not very addictive (see also Van Ours, 2006 for details).

Clearly, prohibition does not work. Cannabis is the most popular illicit drug. The debate on legalisation

Cannabis use: various countries and various measures (percentages)					
LAND	YEAR	AGE	USE EVER	USE LAST YEAR	USE LAST MONTH
Australia	2007	14+	34	9	5
Denmark	2008	16–64	39	6	2
England	2008/9	16–59	31	8	5
France	2005	15–64	31	9	5
Germany	2006	18–64	23	5	2
Italy	2008	15–64	32	14	7
Netherlands	2009	15–64	26	7	4
Spain	2007/8	15–64	27	10	7
Sweden	2008	15–64	21	1	1
US	2009	12+	42	11	7

Source: Van Laar (2011)

of cannabis is gaining momentum. Caulkins et al. (2012) mention seven motivations for creating a legal cannabis market:

⇨ Raising tax revenues,

⇨ Eliminating arrests,

⇨ Undercutting black markets and associated harms from corruption and violence,

⇨ Redirecting criminal justice resources,

⇨ Assuring product quality,

⇨ Increasing choices for those seeking intoxication, and

⇨ Limiting youth access by better control.

The legalisation debate is often emotional with strong views on both sides. Those who support legalisation tend to ignore the negative health effects of cannabis use. Those opposed ignore the fact that legal substances such as alcohol and tobacco also have bad health effects (Hall and Lynskey, 2009).

The Dutch example

The Netherlands has a cannabis policy that is closest to being legal although cannabis supply and distribution are prohibited; though using cannabis is not legal, it is decriminalised. The main aim of Dutch drug policy is to protect the health of individual users, the people around them and society as a whole. Regulations on drugs are laid down in the Opium Act, which draws a distinction between hard drugs and soft drugs. Hard drugs are those substances which can seriously harm the health of the user and include heroin, cocaine and synthetic drugs such as ecstasy. Soft drugs – i.e. the cannabis derivatives, marijuana and hashish – cause far fewer health problems. The possession of hard drugs is a crime. However, since 1976, the possession of a small quantity of soft drugs for personal use is a minor offence.

The expediency principle is applied to the sale of cannabis in 'coffee shops' in order to separate the users' market for hard and soft drugs and to keep young people who experiment with cannabis away from hard drugs. The sale of small quantities of soft drugs in coffee shops is therefore technically an offence, but prosecution proceedings are only instituted if the operator or owner of the shop does not meet certain criteria. These criteria are that no more than five grammes per person may be sold in any one transaction, no hard drugs may be sold, drugs may not be advertised, the coffee shop must not cause any nuisance, no drugs may be sold to people under 18 and under-18s are not allowed into the premises. Moreover, the mayor may order a coffee shop to be closed.

According to MacCoun (2011) the Dutch coffee shop system may have been responsible for separating the soft and hard drug markets and rather than increasing the gateway from soft to hard drug use may have reduced this gateway (see also Van Ours, 2003). According to Reuter (2010) commercialisation of sale in The Netherlands may have led to an increase in consumption but the increased access has not led to the Dutch population showing higher-than-average rates of cannabis use or longer cannabis-use careers. Korf (2002) indicates that the use of cannabis in The Netherlands shows trends that are very similar to those in other European countries that have not decriminalised cannabis.

Until the middle of the 1970s, coffee shops were largely absent from The Netherlands. Then their number increased rapidly to reach a maximum of about 1,500 across the country in the early 1990s. From 2000 to 2009 the number of coffee shops decreased – in the four big cities (Amsterdam, Rotterdam, Utrecht and The Hague) by 74, and in the rest of The Netherlands by 73. In 2009 in 101 of the Dutch municipalities out of the total of 441 municipalities there were one or more coffee shops (Bieleman and Nijkamp 2010). The reduction in the number of coffee shops has to do with closings near schools and a stricter policy against coffee shops that did not stick to the rules and regulations. In Amsterdam, for example, the number of coffee shops went from 283 in 2000 to 225 in 2009. In some municipalities close to the border, all coffee shops have been closed to avoid 'drug tourism' from Belgium, France and Germany, i.e. to ban foreign customers who buy cannabis in The Netherlands and take this across the border. According to Wouters et al. (2010) there has been a shift in policy from a health perspective to a law-and-order perspective. They find that the presence of coffee shops in a municipality is more likely in large municipalities and municipalities with a left-wing local government while the number of coffee shops in a municipality is mainly determined by its population size.

Because supply and distribution of cannabis is still prohibited, policy in The Netherlands is in a twilight zone. Recently, measures have been implemented to reduce access to coffee shops. The plan is to transform the coffee shops to clubs for which one needs a permit to enter. The main idea of these permits is that they will prevent tourists from entering, thus making coffee shops local shops for local people.

California Proposition 19

According to Kilmer et al. (2010) California has always been on the cutting edge of cannabis-policy reform. In 1975, California reduced the maximum sentence for possessing less than an ounce (28.35 grammes) of cannabis from incarceration to a small fine. In 1996, California allowed cannabis to be grown and consumed for medical purposes. California currently has over 1,000 medical marijuana shops. In November 2010, California voted on whether cannabis should be legalised and taxed. The Californian Proposition on the 2010 ballot – the Regulate, Control, and Tax Cannabis Act, also known as Proposition 19 – would have fully legalised cannabis with respect to the Californian state law. It would not have prevented federal prohibition action. In theory, federal agents can take over low-level enforcement but in practice federal prosecutors would probably only deal with large quantities of cannabis.

Rosalie Pacula (2010) argues that the debate on cannabis legalisation in California is dominated by worries about health consequences as one fifth of all treatment admissions in the state is due to marijuana use. An increase in cannabis use may also cause an increase in health expenditures paid through taxes. So a priori it is not clear that there will be a net tax reduction if cannabis is legalised. However, she concludes that it is unlikely that a rise in the known health harms would lead to a large enough cost to taxpayers to offset the revenue gain from legalising and taxing – assuming that taxes are actually paid and not evaded. Kilmer et al. (2010) provide estimates of the possible effects of legalising cannabis in California. Taking into account that their estimates have unknown confidence intervals they find that the pre-tax retail price of cannabis will decrease, likely by more than 80%. The effect on consumer prices will depend on taxes but it is likely that consumption will go up. Tax revenues will increase but it is virtually impossible to indicate by how much. The savings on enforcing cannabis laws are also difficult to indicate. Caulkins et al. (2012) take Proposition 19 as their inspiration to discuss legalisation design choices – i.e. the level of taxes and whether taxes should depend on cannabis levels, rules on home cultivation, advertising restrictions and design adjustments over time. They argue that taxes should be sufficiently high to discourage cannabis use and sufficiently low to drive out illegal supply. Furthermore, taxes should depend on cannabinoid levels, home cultivation should be allowed under restrictions and advertising should be banned. The most important design choice of legalisation is the flexibility to adjustment, allowing for learning by doing.

Proposition 19 was narrowly rejected with 53.5% of the voters voting against the proposal.

Health effects of cannabis use

Worries about cannabis often relate to the connection between cannabis use and crime. Little is known about the subject but cannabis-induced crime by users seems to be limited (organised crime is however heavily involved in supplying cannabis use). Furthermore, there is a discussion about whether cannabis use induces the use of hard drugs, but this 'stepping-stone' effect seems to be absent or small (Van Ours, 2003). People mainly worry about the health effects of cannabis use. Nevertheless, in the grand scheme of risky health behaviours, cannabis use has a modest contribution (Cawley and Ruhm, 2011).

From a meta-analysis, Degenhardt et al. (2003) conclude that there seems to be a modest but significant association between heavy use of cannabis and later depression. In their overview study, Arseneault et al. (2004) conclude that rates of cannabis use are approximately twice as high among people with schizophrenia as among the general population. Hall and Degenhardt (2009) argue that previous research on the relationship between mental health

and illicit substance use comes almost entirely from epidemiology. The results from this research are mixed, with some papers reporting a positive association between cannabis use and mental health problems and others reporting no association. Discussing a variety of papers Werb et al. (2010) conclude that the research to date is insufficient to conclusively claim that the association between cannabis use and psychosis is causal in nature.

In examining the relationship between mental health and cannabis use, the literature cited above has attempted to identify the causal effect of cannabis use by controlling for observed factors that may be a source of confounding. However, as noted by Pudney (2010), the potential for unobserved common confounding factors makes inference regarding the causal impact of cannabis use difficult. Nevertheless, recent evidence suggests that there is a negative causal effect of cannabis use on health (Van Ours and Williams, 2011a and 2011b).

All of the linkages to assess the health effects of legalisation have one element in common: uncertainty. Therefore, opinions of people with personal experience of cannabis use may be helpful. From an analysis of Australian data it appears that past cannabis users are more in favour of legalisation than non-users. Apparently for individuals with personal experience the personal benefits of legalisation are more important than the personal costs (Williams et al. 2011).

The long and winding road

Caulkins et al. (2012), argue that prohibition of rarely used substances is easier to implement than prohibition of widely used drugs. This also applies in reverse. Legalisation of a frequently used drug such as cannabis will have smaller effects on use than legalising a less frequently used

drug such as cocaine. However, the discussion about legalisation of cannabis is hampered because even simple effects are not clear in terms of their magnitude. It is most likely that cannabis prices will go down and cannabis use will go up. But whether this will induce negative health effects depends on whether the increase in use will be at the intensive margin as well as the extensive margin. Criminal activities, predominantly those by suppliers, will be reduced. Whether the benefits of legalisation outweigh its costs will also depend on design choices.

There are many relationships about which researchers are uncertain, debating whether they are causal or mere associations. Removing the veil of ignorance that surrounds the legalisation debate requires much more research effort. However, researchers rarely agree, and even if they would agree it is doubtful whether that would convince politicians to go ahead with cannabis legalisation. Doing further research and hoping that an evidence-based cannabis policy will emerge is wishful thinking. Rather than muddling through for several decades it would be wise to start moving on the long and winding road to cannabis legalisation.

The health effects of cannabis use should not be ignored. Clearly, it is healthier not to use cannabis at all. Nevertheless, the health effects should not be exaggerated either. If alcohol use and smoking cigarettes are accepted, albeit under restrictions, then so should cannabis use. There are clear advantages to legalisation. Legalisation would make life more comfortable for cannabis users, remove criminal organisations from the scene, allow for the possibility of quality control, provide governments with tax revenues and make it possible for researchers to collect empirical evidence. In short, it is time for politicians to walk down the legalisation road 'to boldly go where no man has gone before' (Van Ours, 2012).

References

Bieleman B and N Nijkamp (2010). *Coffeeshops in Nederland 2009*, Intraval, Rotterdam.

Caulkins JP, B Kilmer, RJ MacCoun, RL Pacula and P Reuter (2012). 'Design considerations for legalizing cannabis: Lessons inspired by analysis of California's proposition 19', *Addiction*, 107: 865-871.

Cawley J and C Ruhm (2011). 'The economics of risky health behaviors', *NBER Working Paper* No. 17081.

Degenhardt L, W Hall and M Lynskey (2003). 'Exploring the association between cannabis use and depression', *Addiction*, 98:1493-1504.

Hall W and L Degenhardt (2009). 'The adverse health effects of non-medical cannabis use'. *Lancet*, 374:1383-1391.

Hall W and M Lynskey (2009). 'The challenges in developing a rational cannabis policy', *Current Opinion in Psychiatry*, 22:258-262.

Kilmer B, JP Caulkins, RL Pacula, RJ MacCoun and PH Reuter (2010). 'Altered State?', *Occasional Paper Rand*.

Korf DJ (2002). 'Dutch coffee shops and trends in cannabis use', *Addictive Behaviors*, 27:851-866.

MacCoun RJ (2011). 'What can we learn from the Dutch cannabis coffeeshop system?', *Addiction*, 106:1899-1910.

Pacula RL (2010). 'Examining the impact of marijuana legalization on harms associated with marijuana use', *RAND Working Paper* WR-769-RC.

Pudney S (2010). 'Drugs policy – what should we do about cannabis?', *Economic Policy*, 61:165-211.

Reuter P (2010). 'Marijuana legalization: what can be learned from other countries?', *RAND Working Paper* WR-771-RC.

United Nations Office on Drugs and Crime (2011). *World Drugs Report*, United Nations, New York.

Van Laar MW (2011). *Nationale Drug Monitor*, Trimbos-Instituut, Utrecht.

Van Ours JC (2003). 'Is cannabis a stepping-stone for cocaine?', *Journal of Health Economics*, 22:539-554.

Van Ours JC (2006). 'Dynamics in the use of drugs', *Health Economics*, 15:1283-1294.

Van Ours JC (2012). 'The long and winding road to cannabis legalization', *Addiction*, 107, forthcoming.

Van Ours JC and J Williams (2011a). 'Cannabis use and mental health problems', *Journal of Applied Econometrics*, 26:1137-1156.

Van Ours JC and J Williams (2011b). 'The effects of cannabis use on physical and mental health', *CEPR Discussion Paper* No. 8499.

Werb, D, B Fischer, and E Wood (2010). 'Cannabis policy: time to move beyond the psychosis debate', *International Journal of Drug Policy*, 21:261-264.

Williams J, JC Van Ours, and M Grossman (2011). 'Why do some people want to legalize cannabis use?', *NBER Working Paper* No. 11-07.

Wouters M, A Benschop and DJ Korf (2010). 'Local politics and retail cannabis markets: the case of Dutch coffeeshops', *International Journal of Drug Policy*, 21:315-320.

6 December 2011

Should the UK legalise cannabis?

Yes!

Damon Applegate – Cannabis smoker

My Dad was an alcoholic and died from it. I choose not to drink alcohol (which is also a drug!). I don't really like the effects and I think it makes people loud and aggressive. It's also really bad for your health. I enjoy having the odd joint instead. I think cannabis is much more natural and it makes me relaxed and also think more creatively.

Fact: Cannabis has been smoked for thousands of years and there has never been a known fatal overdose.

Issue: I'm not harming anyone. I just like the feeling of getting stoned sometimes. I don't think the law has any business saying I can't.

Question: Yes, dope makes you laidback, but is that such a bad thing? All this 'progress' is destroying the planet – using up resources, causing global warming. What's wrong with people chilling out a bit?

Jess Baker – Probation officer

I work with young people who've been released from prison. Going to prison can be a horrible experience for a young person and very destructive. It interrupts their education, brings them into contact with more serious criminals and gives them a criminal record which can make it hard to get a job.

Fact: 8.9% of 11- to 15-year-olds say they have smoked cannabis in the last year.

Issue: Using cannabis is quite common – It breaks my heart to see so many young lives ruined for something I personally think is not that serious a crime.

Question: People say it's a 'gateway drug', but the evidence is weak that using cannabis CAUSES people to then use harder drugs. Most people drink alcohol before they try any other drugs. Is alcohol a gateway drug, or is it just widely available?

No!

Jenny Bellamy – Psychiatrist

I work in a mental hospital with people who have schizophrenia. It can be very scary for them and their families and really mess their lives up. I believe using cannabis makes people more likely to get schizophrenia so I'd like less people to take it.

Fact: Cannabis use is about twice as common in people with schizophrenia, compared to people who don't.

Issue: I think if cannabis was legal it would be easier to get hold of and more people would take it, and it could harm them.

Question: It's all very well to say people are taking it anyway, and we may as well tax it. But you could say the same thing about anything! What about child porn, or hiring a hit man?

Stuart Kelly – Father

My son died of a heroin overdose a year ago. He'd been a bright boy at school, but got in with the wrong crowd. He started off smoking cannabis, dropped out of school and ended up getting into harder and harder drugs and a worse life style. He was only 25 when he died but he looked much older.

Fact: In one experiment, scientists gave cannabis to adolescent rats. When those same rats were adults, they gave them access to heroin. The cannabis rats took more heroin than the control group.

Issue: I think cannabis is a 'gateway drug'. Drug-taking is a slippery slope and we should stop people starting on it!

Question: You can say it's bad to give young people a criminal record, but shall we just get rid of all the laws then? Make murder legal so that murderers don't have a criminal record?

⇨ The above information is reprinted with kind permission from *I'm a Scientist Get me out of here*, created by Gallomanor and funded by the Wellcome Trust. Please visit debate.imascientist.org.uk for further information.

© I'm a Scientist Get me out of here 2013

'Legalise it, don't criticise it' – should cannabis be legalised?

By Dr Nicholas M. Almond

The above lyrics are taken from a Bob Marley/ Peter Tosh song which has been covered by UB40 entitled *Legalise It*; arguing for the legalisation of cannabis. The issue of drug use has been discussed recently due to critics arguing that events such as Glastonbury promote the culture of illegal drug taking. I can picture many of you, who are perhaps a bit naive when it comes to drug use reading this with a look of disgust on your face, but let's just consider the facts for a moment before we jump to the conclusion that if cannabis is legalised the UK will become a massive drugs ghetto with tens of millions of people suffering from mental health issues such as schizophrenia.

One argument against the legalisation of cannabis is the 'evidence' which links the use of cannabis to the development of schizophrenia. Please note that I use the word links and not causes – this is very important as I hope I will be able to explain. Even the most hard-line right-wing so-called experts in mental health will admit that only a small proportion of schizophrenia cases can be accounted for by the use of cannabis. Yes, unfortunately the majority of cases of schizophrenia can be accounted for by genetic factors, brain development disorders and chronic stress.

So, why are certain groups so convinced by the evidence that cannabis can cause schizophrenia? First we need to understand the neurological basis of schizophrenia (don't worry, I will not get too technical here). Schizophrenia is caused by an imbalance in a neurotransmitter called dopamine, particularly in the frontal-lobes and limbic system of the brain. If you give a person with schizophrenia drugs which increase dopamine across the whole brain, their symptoms worsen. Specifically, people with schizophrenia show a decrease in dopamine levels in the frontal cortex of the brain and an increase in dopamine levels in the limbic region of the brain which is responsible for many functions including addiction.

Smoking tobacco releases nicotine which stimulates the release of dopamine in the frontal cortex of the brain, therefore there is no surprise that there is a very high correlation between smoking and schizophrenia. Here comes the uncomplicated part: drug dealers tend to target younger adults who smoke. These drug dealers begin with selling cannabis before pushing other more dangerous drugs to the buyer. These drugs tend to begin with ecstasy and LSD, then build up to coke and, if the person is really unlucky, heroin.

I can hear all my anti-drug campaigners screaming out 'See cannabis does lead to people taking harder drugs!' No, that is simply only because cannabis is illegal. Believe it or not, one does not have a joint or chocolate brownie and then think 'Ooh, I will take some crack cocaine tomorrow.' The majority of people who enjoy cannabis do not want any other drugs such as ecstasy, speed or coke, because these are uppers (drugs which excite you and give you more energy; and definitely do not help you relax). Cannabis on the other hand is similar to alcohol in that people who take it mainly do so to help them relax.

So, how about the quality of the cannabis which you get from your local dealer? Unfortunately, if you smoke resin you will find that quite a lot of that little black block is made up of tarmac, plastic bags and even dog excretions (lovely!). If you smoke skunk then the probability is that you have a lot of stuff which is a nice green or yellow colour which will burn in it. This includes nylon carpets, a number of herbs (excuse the pun) and anything else which the dealers can get hold of to spread out their packet of dope which you are buying. Yes, unfortunately the cannabis which is available on the street is probably only 40 to 50% cannabis, if that.

Let's reconsider the argument for the relationship between cannabis and schizophrenia; is it at all possible that the rubbish that dealers use to make the cannabis go further causes damage to the brain? I don't think inhaling plastic bags, dog poo or nylon carpet does anyone any good. There is also the case that the dealers will push other drugs onto the buyers, and it is well known that cocaine and drugs like that have a massive effect on dopamine in the brain. We are also forgetting the relationship between smoking and schizophrenia; even when the schizophrenia has not become apparent these people tend to smoke more, just they are targeted by the drug dealers and a lot of drug dealers are not the kind of people you would take home to meet your mother. A lot of drug dealers are also associated with money lending and organised crime and if a person who has a genetic predisposition to schizophrenia becomes entangled in this the only result is an increase in stress, which brings on the schizophrenia.

Okay let's lay off the friendly dealers for a moment and look at this in a different perspective. If cannabis was legalised, then the Government could control the strength of the drug and users would know what they were taking. This is the case in The Netherlands where cannabis is legal; you can eat it, drink it in tea or smoke it in a joint; but you know what kind you are having and how strong it is in terms of THC (the active ingredient in cannabis which stimulates dopamine and GABBA-a release in the medial temporal lobe and brain stem). Now, if cannabis causes schizophrenia one would expect a higher rate of schizophrenia in The Netherlands compared to the UK where cannabis is illegal. Whoops, that is not the case according to a report by the World Health Organization; in 2004 the WHO calculated the disability-adjusted life years for all countries and reported the diagnosis of both physical and mental illnesses per head of the population. For schizophrenia, we are looking on a scale from the lowest, which was Australia with 164.225 per 100,000 to the highest, Indonesia that has 321.870. So let's compare the cannabis smoking Dutch to the stiff upper-lipped British; The Netherlands had 168.282 while in the UK the diagnosis of schizophrenia per 100,000 was 185.182. You do not need to be a mathematical genius to see that where cannabis is legal and regulated the diagnosis of schizophrenia is lower than where it is not regulated and illegal.

Finally, let's consider the number of deaths caused by legal drugs compared to cannabis. According to national statistics, in 2011 just below 8,750 deaths were the direct cause of alcohol. If one would like to read, 100,000 died from smoking every year. How many died directly from cannabis overdose? The answer is a big fat 0! It is physically impossible to overdose on cannabis. Furthermore, it is physically impossible to become addicted to the active ingredients of cannabis because THC has such a long half-life that you do not become physically dependent upon it, unlike alcohol and nicotine. Yes, okay you can become psychologically addicted to cannabis, but you can also become psychologically addicted to anything from alcohol to chocolate (regardless of whether it is legal or illegal). There is also the cost of alcohol and smoking on the NHS; according to *The Daily Mail* alcohol abuse costs the NHS £6 billion a year, and according to the BBC News, smoking costs the NHS £5 billion a year. It is true that schizophrenia costs the NHS £6.7 billion a year, according to NICE (but only a tiny amount of this can arguably be the direct result of cannabis, if any at all).

Professor David Nutt lost his job for suggesting legalising cannabis; but if the former chair of the Advisory Council on the Misuse of Drugs does not know what he is on about then there is something wrong. Sure, many of you will be moaning that if cannabis is legalised then we are advocating smoking; that does not have to be the case, for example you could legalise cannabis for the consumption in food and drink in cafes for individuals who are aged 18 and over. The tax revenue which we would raise from cannabis could be used to treat schizophrenia, educate children on the misuse of drugs and help to reduce the Government's deficit. Let's face the truth, the US had to end prohibition due to the fact that the sale of illegal alcohol was massive and funding criminal organisations, as well as killing hundreds of people with highly toxic beverages such as moonshine; so when are we going to get a grip and legalise cannabis... and relax?

5 July 2013

⇨ The above information is reprinted with kind permission from Dr Nicholas M Almond. Please feel free to contact Dr Almond, via *The Huffington Post UK*, for further information. www.huffingtonpost.co.uk.

Smoking cannabis can lead to harder drugs

By Danny McCubbin, Founders of the UK San Patrignano Association

I knew something was up with the person who was supposed to meet me today at 11.30am when there was no sign of him just around 11.45. The lad in question had reached out to me for help as his life was spiralling out of control because of drugs. Like so many other young people who I work with who are addicted to drugs, the lad who I was supposed to meet today smoked cannabis at a young age that led him to trying harder drugs. Yesterday I read Nicholas Almond's blog calling for the legalisation of cannabis. Reading your blog Nicholas you sound like quite a decent person but I can't help wondering to myself if you have ever had to deal with someone who is addicted to heroin because they decided to smoke cannabis when they were young? Or have you ever sat with a parent who is in tears because their daughter is lying in hospital fighting for her life as a result of a heroin overdose? I have and I can tell you here and now that I think it is a huge mistake to legalise cannabis use because I have seen and witnessed first hand how smoking cannabis at a young age can ruin a person's life. Instead of saying to our young that it is acceptable to smoke cannabis we need to educate them to make better choices and to inform them of the dangers of taking drugs.

I am learning a great deal about addiction as a result of the work that I am doing in establishing the San Patrignano Association here in the UK. Some of the stories that the addicts tell me are shocking and downright infuriating. Two people now have told me that one of the best places for drug dealers to deal is to wait outside NA meetings and to follow those brave souls who are doing their best to rid themselves of their addictions forever to sell them drugs. I am also working with another lad in Bradford who finds it impossible to get away from drug dealers as they continually offer him free crack and heroin to test in order to grade it. What hope and chance does this lad have?

I work with anyone who is addicted to drugs and I also help the young people from San Patrignano to come to the UK to find work and start a life for themselves here. They continually guide me and teach me valuable lessons so that I am able to help addicts enter San Patrignano. Their experience and skills are not based on any textbook or degree, rather they know first hand how to deal with addicts and importantly how to help them because of what they have experienced and the lessons that they have learnt. Having said that I don't think for a minute that any of them could have helped me today, for when I finally got hold of the lad who I was supposed to meet he was distraught as he had been up all night drinking. He said that he had not taken any drugs and he certainly was not in a fit state to meet with me to discuss entering a long-term residential drug rehabilitation community where the residents stay for a minimum of four years.

The boy today was completely lost and for an hour and a half I waited for him. We both gave up in the end; he was crying and he said to me that he had tried so hard to get to the tube station where I was waiting for him. I am here if he needs me but in truth I know he has a long way to go before he enters the community in Italy as he could not even stay sober to make our meeting. As I took the tube home and reflected on Nicholas's blog and my day I could not but help think what this lad's life would have been like if he had not smoked his first joint? To Nicholas and anyone else who is reading this who thinks that it's a good idea to legalise cannabis please take the time to read Achim's blog. He is a young resident and a good friend of mine who is about to leave San Patrignano. He too smoked cannabis at a young age and now he has his life back thanks to the hard work that he did to finish his time at San Patrignano. Finally, if you have some time please watch my video on San Patrignano – it has a 72% success rate and it is completely free.

9 July 2013

⇨ The above information is reprinted with kind permission from *The Huffington Post UK*. Please visit www.huffingtonpost.co.uk for further information.

© 2013 AOL (UK) Limited

53% of GB public want cannabis legalised or decriminalised

New Ipsos MORI poll shows 53% of GB public want cannabis legalised or decriminalised.

By Peter Reynolds

A new poll by Ipsos MORI, commissioned by Transform Drug Policy Foundation, shows that over half of the public (53%) support cannabis legalisation (legal regulation of production and supply) or decriminalisation of possession of cannabis. Only one in seven support heavier penalties and more being spent on enforcement for cannabis offences. In addition, the survey shows that around two thirds (67%) support a comprehensive independent review of all the possible policy options (from legal market regulation to tougher enforcement) for controlling drugs.

The findings indicate that 45% of mid-market newspaper readers (including *Daily Mail* and *Express* readers) support cannabis legalisation (legal regulation of production and supply) or decriminalisation of possession of cannabis, with less than one in five (17%) supporting heavier penalties and more being spent on enforcement for cannabis offences. For tabloid readers these figures are 47% and 20%. Around 65% of mid-market newspaper readers and 66% of tabloid readers support a full review of all drug policy options.

Additional survey findings include:

⇨ 53% of the public support legal regulation or decriminalisation of cannabis – 50% of Conservative supporters and 55% of Labour supporters also support these options, as do 46% of *Daily Mail* readers

⇨ Only 14% of the public (and 17% of *Daily Mail* readers) support tougher enforcement and heavier penalties for cannabis offences

⇨ 67% want a comprehensive review of all policy options. 70% of Conservative supporters and 69% of Labour supporters also feel this way, as do 61% of *Daily Mail* readers

⇨ When outcomes from Portugal were briefly described, almost 40% of the public support the Portuguese-style decriminalisation of small quantities of drugs for personal possession.

A spokesperson for Transform said:

'These results show just how far ahead of politicians the public are. Whilst Labour and Conservative politicians shy away from the debate on drugs, around half of their supporters want to see legal regulation of cannabis production and supply or decriminalisation of cannabis possession, and a significant majority want a comprehensive review of our approach to drugs – including consideration of legal regulation. The poll

demonstrates that even amongst *Daily Mail* readers, almost half support less punitive approaches to cannabis, and a majority back an independent review of all options, which may come as a surprise to the paper's editors.

'Politicians have repeated their "tough on drugs" propaganda for so long that they assume the public are more fearful of change than they really are. In fact the world has changed, and the public are far more progressive than was thought, right across the political spectrum. At the very least the Government should heed long-standing and growing calls for a review of all policy options, including legal regulation. And as a matter of urgency the Coalition should engage in experiments in the Portuguese-style decriminalisation of possession of drugs for personal use. Now is the time for the heads of all parties to show the leadership citizens surely deserve.'

The full poll data is available here: http://www.tdpf.org. uk/Ipsos_MORI_TPDF_poll.pdf.

20 February 2013

⇨ The above information is reprinted with kind permission from CLEAR UK. Please visit www. clear-uk.org for further information.

Police issue cannabis scratch cards to help residents sniff out drug farms

By Emma McFarnon

Cannabis 'scratch and sniff' cards are to be sent to thousands of households in a bid to help people spot hidden marijuana farms.

The cards, which release the odour of cannabis when scratched, are being sent out by Crimestoppers as part of a campaign to tackle cannabis cultivation in the UK.

Police say illegal drug farms are a growing crime – there was a 15 per cent increase in cannabis factories in 2011/12.

It is hoped the cards, which produce the exact smell cannabis plants produce when they are growing, will allow citizens to recognise the odour and call the police if they notice it.

The cards are being sent to 13 areas of England where the number of marijuana plantations have traditionally been highest – Avon & Somerset; Greater Manchester; Hertfordshire; Humberside; Kent; London; Merseyside; Northamptonshire; Nottinghamshire; South Yorkshire; Suffolk; West Midlands and West Yorkshire.

West Yorkshire police area had the largest number of cannabis plantations uncovered in the UK.

The initiative started three years ago in Holland, where 30,000 scratch cards were distributed to homes.

A UK 2012 report found residential properties are increasingly being used to grow cannabis plants.

The Association of Chief Police Officers (ACPO) lead for drugs, Andy Bliss, said: 'Closing down cannabis farms and arresting the criminals who run and organise them is a key focus in drugs policing.

'This is because we recognise that these farms are often run by organised criminals but also because they bring crime and anti-social behaviour into local communities causing real harm and leaving people feeling unsafe.

'We also know that many people don't realise that the empty, run down house or flat on their street with people coming and going late at night may actually be a commercial cannabis farm. It's not just the stereotype of the remote rural set or disused industrial estate unit.

'The Crimestoppers campaign will help members of the public to recognise the signs and smell of a cannabis farm.

'The police will use the intelligence generated by the campaign to help build on recent successes in tackling this issue.'

Founder and Chairman of Crimestoppers, Lord Ashcroft KCMG PC, said: 'Cannabis farms grow more than just drugs. Those who are cultivating cannabis tend to be involved in other areas of crime and are often involved in related gang crime and other violent crimes involving firearms.

'These individuals use violence and intimidation to carry out these crimes and endanger the lives of those around them. We want to help put an end to this and the funding that cultivation provides to serious organised crimes like human trafficking and gun crime.'

Crimestoppers Director of Operations Roger Critchell said: 'We are distributing "scratch and sniff" cards because not many people know how to recognise the signs of cannabis cultivation happening in their neighbourhood.

'Many are also not familiar with the established links between this crime and serous organised crime.'

As a class B drug, supplying cannabis in the UK can lead to a 14-year prison sentence.

Aside from the smell, signs a property is housing a cannabis farm include constantly covered or blocked-off windows; unsociable coming and going at all hours and lots of people visiting; strong and constant lighting day and night and high levels of heat and condensation.

There may also be a constant buzz of ventilation and lots of power cables – gangs dig underground to lay cables which hook up to lamp posts so they don't have to pay for the enormous amounts of electricity they use.

Crimestoppers is asking members of the public to pass on any information about cannabis farms anonymously by telephoning 0800 555 111 or via our anonymous online form via www.crimestoppers-uk.org.

Both routes are anonymous – names are not taken, calls and IP addresses are not traced or recorded and people do not have to go to court.

19 March 2013

⇨ The above information is reprinted with kind permission from This is Staffordshire (*The Sentinel*). Please visit www.thisisstaffordshire.co.uk for further information.

Key facts

- Half of all 16- to 29-year-olds have tried cannabis at least once. (page 1)

- The maximum penalty for cannabis possession is a five-year prison sentence or an unlimited fine. (page 2)

- The maximum penalty for dealing/supplying cannabis is a 14-year prison sentence or an unlimited fine. (page 2)

- There are about 400 chemical compounds in an average cannabis plant. (page 2)

- A higher percentage of boys than girls use cannabis (although this is minimal). (page 5)

- In the 1920s, recreational use of marijuana was banned in the UK. (page 7)

- There are between 1.7 million and 3.6 million active cannabis users in the UK consuming between 620 and 1,400 metric tonnes of cannabis each year. (page 10)

- The estimated value of the cannabis market in the UK is between £2.9 and £8.6 billion per year. (page 10)

- The majority of the UK market is accounted for by cannabis domestically produced in the UK, with an estimate of between 167,000 and 410,000 UK growers producing between 390 and 950 metric tonnes of cannabis per year. (page 10)

- Around one in ten cannabis users have unpleasant experiences including confusion, hallucinations, anxiety and paranoia. (page 11)

- For regular, long-term, cannabis users who are withdrawing from cannabis use: three out of four experience cravings; half become irritable; seven out of ten switch to tobacco in an attempt to stay off cannabis. (page 12)

- Approximately 20 million adults, or around 6% of the population aged 15- to 64-years-old have used cannabis in the last year. (page 15)

- Of the estimated three million European daily cannabis users, roughly 70% are aged between 15 and 34, and over 86% of clients entering treatment in Europe with cannabis as their primary drug are aged 34 or less. (page 16)

- More than three-quarters of all reported drug law offences in the European Union are related to cannabis, and this figure has been increasing since 2006. (page 17)

- In 2012 a research team surveyed the customers of four medical marijuana dispensaries in British Columbia, Canada. Three quarters of them said they substitute cannabis for at least one other substance. 41% of them substitute it for alcohol, 36% for illicit substances, and 68% for prescription drugs. (page 18)

- 35% of respondents to a YouGov survey in January 2013 would 'strongly favour' allowing doctors to prescribe small amounts of marijuana for their patients. (page 19)

- Cannabis smoking poses a 20-times greater risk of lung cancer per cigarette than tobacco smoking. (page 21)

- In the UK it is illegal to sell, possess, grow or distribute cannabis without a licence. (page 27)

- In 2012 the Home Affairs Select Committee recommended reclassification of cannabis back to class C. (page 27)

- 53% of the public support legal regulation or decriminalisation of cannabis. (page 38)

- Only 14% of the public support tougher enforcement and heavier penalties for cannabis offences. (page 38)

Cannabis

Cannabis is the most widely used illegal drug in Britain. Made from parts of the cannabis plant, it's a naturally occurring drug. It is a mild sedative (often causing a chilled-out feeling or actual sleepiness) and it's also a mild hallucinogen (meaning users may experience a state where they see objects and reality in a distorted way and may even hallucinate). The main active compound in cannabis is tetrahydrocannabinol (THC). Slang names include dope, ganja, grass, hash, marijuana, weed and pot.

Herbal cannabis (grass or weed)

This is made from the dried leaves and flowering parts of the female plant and looks like tightly packed dried herbs.

Medicinal cannabis

There is evidence that cannabis use alleviates the painful symptoms of some diseases, such as Multiple Sclerosis and Arthritis. This is a controversial subject, as many believe those with debilitating illness should not be prosecuted if they are using cannabis for pain relief. However, others say that the law must apply to everyone or its impact is weakened.

Mental health

There is some evidence that cannabis use can result in negative mental health outcomes. In the short term, it can cause paranoia, and for those with a pre-existing mental illness such as schizophrenia, it can contribute to a relapse. In addition, those with a family background of mental illness may be at increased risk of developing a psychotic illness through cannabis use.

Multiple Sclerosis (MS)

A condition of the central nervous system in which the immune system attacks itself.

Reclassification

There are three categories of illegal substance, classes A, B and C, and drugs are classified according to how harmful they are known to be to users and society. Class A drugs are considered to be the most dangerous, and use or supply of these substances will incur a harsher criminal penalty. Class C drugs are the least harmful, but are nevertheless considered dangerous enough to be illegal. Cannabis was reclassified in 2004 from a class B to a class C drug. However, in 2008 it was again reclassified back to class B. On both occasions, reclassification has been hotly debated.

Resin (hash)

'Hash' is a blackish-brown lump made from the resin of the cannabis plant. In the past, this was the commonest form of cannabis in the UK, but this is no longer the case. Herbal cannabis (and especially powerful skunk strains) is now the most common form of cannabis used in the UK.

Skunk

This is a high-strength herbal cannabis. There is evidence that skunk has been increasing in THC content over the past three decades, resulting in stronger, more harmful cannabis. While previously resin was more common, skunk now dominates the UK cannabis market. Although the term 'skunk' was originally applied to specific strains of strong-smelling herbal cannabis, the term is now often applied to any type of very potent herbal cannabis.

THC

THC is an abbreviation of delta-9-tetrahydrocannabinol. This is the main psychoactive ingredient in cannabis and leads to the feeling of being 'stoned'. The higher the concentration of this chemical, the more potent the strain of cannabis. It is because of this ingredient that cannabis is one of the most easily detectable drugs when carrying out drugs tests, as THC can take weeks to clear from the body.

Assignments

Brainstorming

⇨ In small groups, brainstorm and create a poster that demonstrates everything you know about cannabis. You should consider the following questions:

  ⇨ What is cannabis?

  ⇨ What are the effects of cannabis use?

  ⇨ Why might someone decide to try cannabis?

  ⇨ Are there any positive effects of using cannabis?

Research

⇨ The article on page 1 says that 'half of all 16- to 29-year-olds have tried cannabis at least once.' Design a questionnaire to find out about cannabis use in your school. The questionnaire should be anonymous and you should aim to find out how many people have tried cannabis and how many people regularly use it, plus three additional questions of your choice. If you are able to distribute your questionnaire: gather your results and write a summary of your findings, using graphs and tables to help display your information.

⇨ Choose another country and research its laws surrounding cannabis use. Write some notes and present your information back to your class.

⇨ What are the possible medical uses of cannabis? Have a look at the information in Chapter 2 of this book, but also conduct your own research. Write a summary of your findings.

Design

⇨ Design an information leaflet that will be handed out at your school or college, explaining synthetic cannabinoids and their risks.

⇨ Create a poster campaign that will be displayed in schools and doctors' surgeries, explaining how to look after a friend who has taken cannabis. You might want to read the article on page 9 *Looking after a friend* on cannabis for further information.

⇨ Design a website that will inform young people about cannabis use. Your website should aim to be unbiased and present teenagers with facts rather than opinions. In groups, discuss the kind of information your website would host, what pages you would need and think of a name for your site. Then, write a short plan detailing your ideas and create a logo. Share with the rest of your class.

Oral

⇨ In pairs, role-play a situation in which one of you is a parent and the other is their teenage son/daughter. As the parent, you should try to explain the risks associated with smoking cannabis but give your son/daughter some tips on how to cope with peer pressure in case they are in a situation where they are being encouraged to try drugs and don't want to.

⇨ In the article on page 13, the Royal College of Psychiatrists says 'If you decide to give up cannabis, it may be no more difficult than giving up cigarettes.' Do you think this is an appropriate comparison to make? Is the statement accurate? Discuss in pairs.

⇨ Stage a debate in which half of your class argues that it should be legal to use cannabis and the other argues that it should be illegal.

⇨ Choose one of the illustrations from this book and discuss it with a partner. Do you think the artist has done a good job at representing the issue? What might you have done differently?

⇨ Read *Young people and marijuana* on pages 5 and 6. Do you agree with the statements about young people that are made in the article? Do you think the person who wrote the article understands the reasons why young people might smoke marijuana? Discuss with a partner and then feedback to your class.

Reading/writing

⇨ Write an article for your local newspaper, exploring the possible benefits of taxing the UK cannabis market.

⇨ Imagine you work for a charity that believes marijuana/cannabis should be legally prescribed in small doses for medical conditions such as MS. Write a blog post explaining your charity's point of view and why it is important.

⇨ Read *'Legalise it, don't criticise it' – should cannabis be legalised?* on page 35. What is the author's point of view? What evidence do you have to back up your answer? Write a paragraph summarising your thoughts.

⇨ Imagine that you are strongly against cannabis use, under any circumstances. Write an opinion post, no longer than one page, explaining your point of view and giving evidence to back it up.

Acknowledgements

The publisher is grateful for permission to reproduce the material in this book. While every care has been taken to trace and acknowledge copyright, the publisher tenders its apology for any accidental infringement or where copyright has proved untraceable. The publisher would be pleased to come to a suitable arrangement in any such case with the rightful owner.

Images

Cover, page iii and page 1: iStock, page 2: iStock, page 7 © Mateusz Atroszko, page 12: iStock, page 14 © Mateusz Atroszko, page 18: iStock, page 24: iStock, page 26: iStock, page 27: iStock, page 33 © Yung Huang Yong, page 36: iStock, page 37: MorgueFile, page 38: MorgueFile.

Illustrations

Page 6: Simon Kneebone, page 10: Angelo Madrid, page 19: Don Hatcher, page 23: Simon Kneebone, page 25: Angelo Madrid, page 35: Don Hatcher.

Additional acknowledgements

Editorial on behalf of Independence Educational Publishers by Cara Acred.

With thanks to the Independence team: Mary Chapman, Sandra Dennis, Christina Hughes, Jackie Staines and Jan Sunderland.

Cara Acred

Cambridge, January 2014